all

Poetry Library

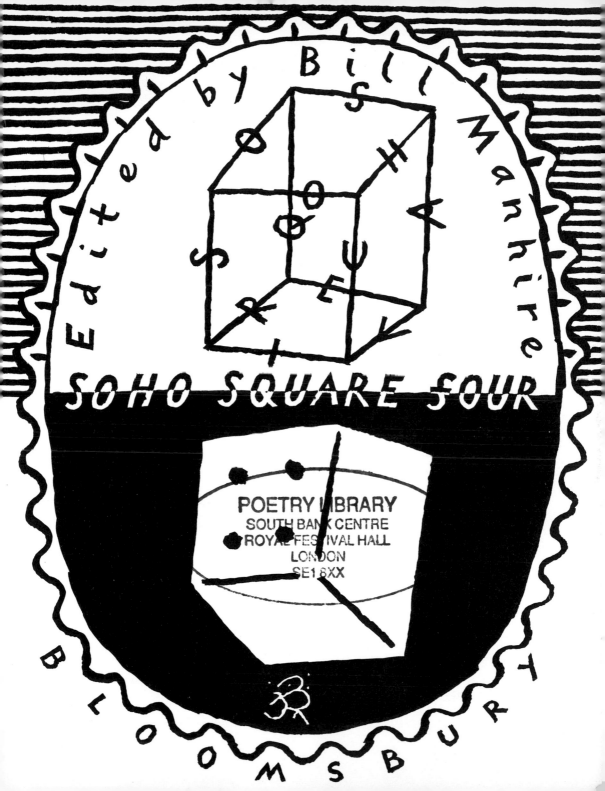

Edited by Bill Manhire

SOHO SQUARE FOUR

BLOOMSBURY

First published 1991
This compilation © 1991 by Bloomsbury Publishing Ltd
The copyright of the individual contributions
remains with the respective authors
The moral right of the authors has been asserted

Bloomsbury Publishing Ltd, 2 Soho Square, London W1V 5DE

A CIP catalogue record for this book
is available from the British Library

ISBN 0 7475 1022 9

Jacket illustration by Jeff Fisher
Designed by Jeff Fisher
Typeset by Falcon Typographic Art Ltd, Edinburgh & London
Printed in Great Britain by Butler & Tanner Ltd, Frome and London

Simeon Dumdum Jr's poems appeared in Tenggara *and* Third World Opera; *Michael Ondaatje's*
poem appeared in Brick; *Gerald Murnane's piece appeared in* Verandah; *John Ashbery's poem*
appeared in Southwest Review.

Lines from 'Oh What is That Sound' from Collected Shorter Poems 1927–1957 *by W. H.*
Auden reprinted by permission of Faber and Faber Ltd.

19/2/97

Contents

Illustrations

STEVEN APPLEBY 63, 211
PETER ARKLE 173
CHRISTINA BRIMAGE 21, 22-23, 56-57, 88-89, 205, 257
CHRISTOPHER BROWN 240-241
BRIAN CAIRNS 90-91
CHLÖE CHEESE 78-79
PAUL DAVIS 19, 77, 86-87, 117, 118-119, 206-207, 237, 267,
268-269, 281
DIRK VAN DOOREN 141
GREG EVERINGHAM 282-283
HERO FISHER 101, 120-121
BRIAN GRIMWOOD 47, 188-189
CLIFFORD HARPER 122-123
ANNE HOWESON 102-103
BENOÎT JACQUES 264-265
JEAN-CHRISTIAN KNAFF 212-213
LAURA KNIGHT 142-143
ANDREW KULMAN 38-39, 278-279
WALTER VAN LOTRINGEN 46
DAVID LUCAS 169
SARAH MAXEY 263
DOURAT BEN-NAHUM 104-105
BRIAN WEBB 11, 49, 114-115, 184-185, 239
ROBIN WHEELAGHAN 74-75

All other illustrations by Jeff Fisher

Introduction

Nearly one hundred years ago Mark Twain – more or less bankrupt and cursed with a carbuncle – did a reading tour of Australia and New Zealand. When he came to write up his travels, the geographical part of his brain felt bound to correct a misconception – that the two countries lay near to one another in the ocean, and that you could cross between them over a bridge. Twain was constructing one or two trans-Tasman bridges of his own as he went, including a poem 'to be read soft and low with the light turned down' which managed to incorporate the musical gurgles of a whole variety of Australasian place-names. This may be why a Wellington journalist challenged him to find a rhyme for Paekakariki, a Maori name which means 'perch of the green parrot', and one for which an earlier literary traveller, Rudyard Kipling, had already failed to find a match.

Bridge-building has always been a useful way to think about the writer's task. There they are – the writer at one end, the reader at the other, and the possibility of traffic in both directions. The idea of bridges serves the aspiring anthologist well, too. But even better, perhaps, is the idea of a room (like one of Twain's stanzas) crammed with incongruities – puzzling sounds, unlikely rhymes, mysterious lists of names. *Soho Square IV* takes heart and impulse from the South Pacific but – like its predecessors – it has wandered about the planet a little, and it sets the work of little-known writers alongside contributions from some of their well-known contemporaries.

Thus the room fills slowly. Interesting people join in conversation – and the fact of company makes them both less and more like themselves. It is nice – for the editorial host, at least – to place the Filipino poet, Simeon Dumdum Jr, between two fiction writers (one from the USA, the other from New Zealand) and notice a moment later that parrots are flickering from text to text. Perhaps this is how Paekakariki finally finds its rhyme.

There are few exotic locations shots here, but there are first things and last things, second skins and second chances, photographs and food, tattoos and angels, wheel-chairs and caretakers, dark horses and various kinds of photo-finish. Unlikely characters make guest appearances – Christopher Columbus, Shirley Temple, Clark Gable (twice!), Joan of Arc, Carl Jung. And alongside the old worlds, there are new worlds and underworlds.

New worlds (see Salman Rushdie's story) eventually lose their glitter, and one day find themselves transformed into the New World Supermarket bags from which Jenny Bornholdt's aunt is busy knitting her broad-brimmed sun-hats. If some of the work here has its shady passages, that is one reason. And if there are moments of darkness, it is worth remembering – as the Samoan writer, Albert

Wendt, makes clear — that *Soho Square IV* was conjured into existence during the Gulf War.

In war, of course, they bomb the bridges, destroying the lines of communication. Writers know where the bridges ought to be, and they go on building them — word by word, phrase by phrase, using whatever they find at hand.

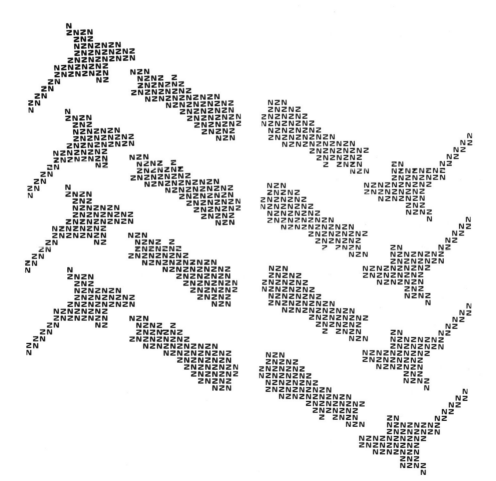

ANGELA CARTER
Ashputtle or The Mother's Ghost:
Three Versions of One Story

a. The Mutilated Girl

But although you could easily take the story away from Ashputtle and centre it on the mutilated sisters – indeed, it would be easy to think of it as a story about cutting bits off women, so that they will *fit in*, some sort of circumcision-like ritual chop, nevertheless, the story always begins not with Ashputtle or her stepsisters but with Ashputtle's mother, as though it is really always the story of her mother even if, at the beginning of the story, the mother herself is just about to exit the narrative because she is at death's door: 'A rich man's wife fell sick, and, feeling that her end was near, she called her only daughter to her bedside.'

Note the absence of the husband/father. Although the woman is defined by her relation to him ('a rich man's wife'), the daughter is unambiguously hers, as if hers alone, and the entire drama concerns only women, takes place almost exclusively among women, is a fight between two groups of women – in the right-hand corner, Ashputtle and her mother; in the left-hand corner, the stepmother and *her* daughters, of whom the father is unacknowledged but all the same is predicated by both textual and biological necessity.

It is a drama between two female families in opposition to one another because of their rivalry over men (husband/father, husband/son), who seem no more than passive victims of their fancy and yet whose significance is absolute because it is ('a rich man', 'a king's son') economic.

Ashputtle's father, the old man, is the first object of their desire and their dissension; the stepmother snatches him from the dead mother before her corpse is cold, as soon as her grip loosens. Then there is the young man, the potential bridegroom, the hypothetical son-in-law, for whose possession the mothers fight, using their daughters as instruments of war or as surrogates in the business of mating.

If the men, and the bank balances for which they stand, are the passive victims of the two grown women, then the girls, all three, are animated solely by the wills of their mothers. Even if Ashputtle's mother dies at the beginning of the story, her status as one of the dead only makes her position more authoritative. The mother's ghost dominates the narrative and is, in a real sense, the motive centre, the event that makes all the other events happen.

On her death bed, the mother assures the daughter, 'I shall always look after you and always be with you.' The story tells you how she does it.

At this point, when her mother makes her promise, Ashputtle is nameless. She is her mother's daughter. That is all we know. It is the stepmother who names her Ashputtle, as a joke, and, in doing so, wipes out her real name, whatever that is, banishes her from the family, exiles her from the shared table to the lonely hearth, among the cinders, removes her contingent but honourable status as daughter and gives her, instead, the contingent but disreputable status of servant.

Her mother told Ashputtle she would always look after her, but then she died and the father married again and gave Ashputtle an imitation mother with daughters of her own whom she loves with the same fierce passion as Ashputtle's mother did and still, posthumously, does, as we shall find out.

With the second marriage comes the vexed question: Who shall be the daughters of the house? Mine! declares the stepmother, and sets the freshly named, non-daughter Ashputtle to sweep and scrub and sleep on the hearth while her daughters lie between clean sheets in Ashputtle's bed. Ashputtle, no longer known as the daughter of her mother, nor of her father either, goes by a dry, dirty, cindery nickname for everything has turned to dust and ashes.

Meanwhile, the false mother sleeps in the bed where the real mother died and is, presumably, pleasured by the husband/father in that bed, unless there is no pleasure in it for her. We are not told what the husband/father does as regards domestic or marital function but we can surely make the assumption that he and the stepmother share a bed because that is what married people do.

And what can the real mother/wife do about it? Burn as she might with love, anger and jealousy, she is dead and buried.

The father, in this story, is a mystery to me. Is he so besotted with his new wife that he cannot see how his daughter is soiled with kitchen refuse and filthy from her ashy bed and always hard at work? If he sensed there was a drama in hand, he was content to leave the entire production to the women for, absent as he might be, always remember that it is *his* house where Ashputtle sleeps on the cinders, and he is the invisible link that binds both sets of mothers and daughters in their violent equation. He is the unmoved mover, the unseen organising principle, like God, and, like God, up he pops in person, one fine day, to introduce the essential plot device.

Besides, without the absent father there would be no story because there would have been no conflict.

If they had been able to put aside their differences and discuss everything amicably, they'd have combined to expel the father. Then all the women could have slept in one bed. If they'd kept the father on, he could have done the housework.

This is the essential plot device introduced by the father: he says, 'I am about to take a business trip. What presents would my three girls like me to bring back for them?'

Note that: his *three* girls.

It occurs to me that perhaps the stepmother's daughters were really, all the time, his own daughters, just as much his own daughters as Ashputtle; his 'natural' daughters, as they say, as though there is something inherently unnatural about legitimacy. *That* would realign the forces in the story. It would make his connivance with the ascendancy of the other girls more plausible. It would make the speedy marriage, the stepmother's hostility, more probable.

But it would also transform the story into something else, because it would provide motivation, and so on; it would mean I'd have to provide a past for all these people, that I would have to equip them with three dimensions, with tastes and memories, and I would have to think of things for them to eat and wear and say. It would transform *Ashputtle* from the bare necessity of fairy-tale, with its characteristic copula formula, 'and then', to the emotional and technical complexity of bourgeois realism. They would have to learn to think. Everything would change.

I will stick with what I know.

What presents do his three girls want?

'Bring me a silk dress,' said his eldest girl. 'Bring me a string of pearls,' said the middle one. What about the third one, the forgotten one, called out of the kitchen on a charitable impulse and drying her hands, raw with housework, on her apron, bringing with her the smell of old fire?

'Bring me the first branch that knocks against your hat on the way home,' said Ashputtle.

Why did she ask for that? Did she make an informed guess at how little he valued her? Or had a dream told her to use this random formula of unacknowledged desire, to allow blind chance to choose her present for her? Unless it was her mother's ghost, awake and restlessly looking for a way home, that came into the girl's mouth and spoke the request for her.

He brought her back a hazel twig. She planted it on her mother's grave and watered it with tears. It grew into a hazel tree. When Ashputtle came out to weep upon her mother's grave, the turtledove crooned, 'I'll never leave you, I'll always protect you.'

Then Ashputtle knew that the turtledove was her mother's ghost and she herself was still her mother's daughter and although she had wept and wailed and longed to have her mother back again, now her heart sank a little to find out that her mother, though dead, was no longer gone, and henceforward she must do her mother's bidding.

Came the time for that curious fair they used to hold in that country, when all the resident virgins went to dance in front of the King's son so that he could pick out the girl he wanted to marry.

The turtledove was mad for that, for her daughter to marry the Prince. You might have thought her own experience of marriage might have taught her to be wary but no, needs must, what else is a girl to do? The turtledove was mad for her daughter to marry so she flew in and picked up the new silk dress with her beak, dragged it to the open window, threw it down to Ashputtle. She did the same with the string of pearls. Ashputtle had a good wash under the pump in the yard, put on her stolen finery and crept out the back way, secretly, to the dancing grounds, but the stepsisters had to stay home and sulk because they had nothing to wear.

The turtledove stayed close to Ashputtle, pecking her ears to make her dance vivaciously, so that the Prince would see her, so that the Prince would love her, so that he would follow her and find the clue of the fallen slipper, for the story is not complete without the ritual humiliation of the other woman and the mutilation of her daughters.

The search for the foot that fits the slipper is essential to the enactment of this ritual humiliation.

The other woman wants that young man desperately. She would do anything to catch him. Not losing a daughter, but gaining a son. She wants a son so badly she is prepared to cripple her daughters. She takes up a carving knife and chops off her elder daughter's big toe, so that her foot will fit the little shoe.

Imagine.

Brandishing the carving knife, the woman bears down on her child, who is as distraught as if she had not been a girl but a boy and the old woman was after a more essential portion than a toe. *No!* she screams. *Mother! No! Not the knife! No!* But off it comes, all the same, and she throws it in the fire, among the ashes, where Ashputtle finds it, wonders at it, and feels both awe and fear at the phenomenon of mother love.

Mother love, which winds about these daughters like a shroud.

The Prince saw nothing familiar in the face of the tearful young woman, one shoe off, one shoe on, displayed to him in triumph by her mother, but he said, 'I promised I would marry whoever the shoe fitted so I will marry you,' and they rode off together.

The turtledove came flying round and did not croon or coo to the bridal pair but sang a horrid song, 'Look! look! There's blood in the shoe!'

The Prince returned the ersatz ex-fiancée at once, angry at the trick, but the stepmother hastily lopped off her other daughter's heel and pushed *that* poor foot into the bloody shoe as soon as it was vacant so, nothing for it, a man of his word, the Prince helped up the new girl and once again he rode away.

Back came the nagging turtledove, 'Look!' And, sure enough, the shoe was full of blood, again.

'Let Ashputtle try,' said the eager turtledove.

So now Ashputtle must put her foot into this hideous receptacle, this open wound, still slick and warm as it is, for nothing in any of the many texts of this tale suggests the Prince washed the shoe out between the fittings. It was an ordeal in itself to put a naked foot into the bloody shoe but her mother, the turtledove, urged her to do so in a soft, cooing croon that could not be denied.

If she does not plunge without revulsion into this open wound, she won't be fit to marry. That was the song of the turtledove, while the other mad mother stood impotently by.

Ashputtle's foot, the size of the bound foot of a Chinese woman, a stump. Almost an amputee already, she put her tiny foot in it.

'Look! Look!' cried the turtledove in triumph, even while the bird betrayed its ghostly nature by becoming progressively more and more immaterial as Ashputtle stood up in the shoe and commenced to walk around. Squelch, went the stump of the foot in the shoe. Squelch. 'Look!' sang out the turtledove. 'Her foot fits the shoe like a corpse fits the coffin.'

'See how well I look after you, my darling!'

b. The Burned Child

A burned child lived in the ashes. No, not really burned, more charred, a little bit charred, like a stick half-burned and picked off the fire. She looked like charcoal and ashes because she lived in the ashes since her mother died and the hot ashes burned her so she was scabbed and scarred. The burned child lived on the hearth, covered in ashes, as if she were still mourning.

After her mother died and was buried, her father forgot the mother and forgot the child and married the woman who used to rake the ashes, and that was why the child lived in the unraked ashes and there was nobody to brush her hair so it stuck out like a mat, nor to wipe the dirt off her scabbed face and she had no heart to do it for herself, but she raked the ashes and slept beside the little cat and got the burned bits from the bottom of the pot to eat, scraping them out, squatting on the floor, by herself in front of the fire, not as if she were human, because she was still mourning.

Her mother was dead and buried but felt perfect exquisite pain of love when she looked up through the earth and saw the burned child covered in ashes.

'Milk the cow, burned child, and bring back all the milk,' said the stepmother, who used to rake the ashes and milk the cow, once upon a time, but the burned child did all that, now.

The ghost of the mother went into the cow.

'Drink milk, grow fat,' said the mother's ghost.

The burned child pulled on the udder and drank enough milk before she took the bucket back and nobody saw, and time passed, she drank milk every day, she grew fat, she grew breasts, she grew up.

There was a man the stepmother wanted, and she asked him into the kitchen to get his dinner but she made the burned child cook it although the stepmother did all the cooking before. After the burned child cooked the dinner the stepmother sent her off to milk the cow.

'I want that man for myself,' said the burned child to the cow.

The cow let down more milk, and more, and more, enough for the girl to have a drink and wash her face and wash her hands. When she washed her face, she washed the scabs off and now she was not burned at all, but the cow was empty.

'Give your own milk next time,' said the ghost of the mother inside the cow. 'You've milked me dry.'

The little cat came by. The ghost of the mother went into the cat.

'Your hair wants doing,' said the cat. 'Lie down.'

The little cat unpicked her raggy lugs with its clever paws until the burned child's hair hung down nicely but it had been so snagged and tangled that the cat's claws were all pulled out before it was finished.

'Comb your own hair next time,' said the cat. 'You've maimed me.'

The burned child was clean and combed but stark naked.

There was a bird sitting in the apple tree. The ghost of the mother left the cow and went into the bird. The bird struck its own breast with its beak. Blood

17

poured down on to the burned child under the tree. It ran over her shoulders and covered her front and covered her back. When the bird had no more blood, the burned child got a red silk dress.

'Make your own dress next time,' said the bird. 'I'm through with that bloody business.'

The burned child went into the kitchen to show herself to the man. She was not burned any more, but lovely. The man left off looking at the stepmother and looked at the girl.

'Come home with me and let your stepmother stay and rake the ashes,' he said to her and off they went. He gave her a house and money. She did all right.

'Now I can go to sleep,' said the ghost of the mother. 'Now everything is all right.'

c. Travelling Clothes

The stepmother took the red-hot poker and burned the orphan's face with it because she had not raked the ashes. The girl went to her mother's grave.

In the earth her mother said, 'It must be raining. Or else it is snowing. Unless there is a heavy dew tonight.'

'It isn't raining, it isn't snowing, it's too early for the dew. My tears are falling on your grave, mother.'

The dead woman waited until night came. Then she climbed out and went to the house. The stepmother slept on a feather bed but the burned child slept on the hearth among the ashes. When the dead woman kissed her, the scar vanished. The girl woke up. The dead woman gave her a red dress.

'I had it when I was your age.'

The girl put the red dress on. The dead woman took worms from her eyesockets; they turned into jewels. The girl put on a diamond ring.

'I had it when I was your age.'

They went together to the grave.

'Step into my coffin.'

'No,' said the girl. She shuddered.

'I stepped into *my* mother's coffin when I was your age.'

The girl stepped into the coffin although she thought it would be the death of her. It turned into a coach and horses. The horses stamped, eager to be gone.

'Go and seek your fortune, darling.'

SHARON THESEN
Two Poems
Chicken in a Pensive Shell

Is really Chicken in a Pineapple Shell, but
glancing at it sideways
while making tea I thought it said,
in a Pensive Shell, a mood
I'm often in, coming from my thought, my
face dark with them as a pansy's.

Pascal in his *Pensées*
says nothing about chicken
but is sure our major distress
derives from having a home, the same old
boring old place where we rot &
rot and thereby hangs a tale.
Of woe, according to Pascal's
pensée, and here it's almost time
to start the chicken, Poulet
Marengo, a favourite
of Napoleon's. He liked it garnished
with crawfish and fried eggs.

As the oven heats up, rosy elements
brighten the tinted window
you look in to see your
nervous soufflé rising or not. No
pensée will help your soufflé
or chicken either, bubbling like lava
in the orange pot, with eight mushrooms,
a cup of white wine, and the empty pineapple
shells arrayed for next time, or next year,
or never. Their pensive moods

attract the wrong sort of chicken
who wear black thongs and carry a knife.
Their shirts are shiny, they belong
to another page, another life.

I prefer my Poulet ungarnished,
with rice, an easy salad on the side.
In a pensive shell will lie
my thoughts, dark inside
where you can't see the ocean
that roars and roars
in Napoleon's sleep. He spread himself
too thin. His crawfish garnish
outmanoeuvred him. I rest my case
on the kitchen counter where books
outnumber saucers & adjacent recipes
clash by night in pineapple shell
rowboats. And Divan gets a whiff
of Marengo and bam! the Duke
of Wellington fires his cannon.

Love & Work

These old friends and I sit around a table
taking a break from the basement renovation's
wet concrete and welding torch and my reading
Bataille's *Erotism: Death and Sensuality*, birds
twittering outside in the sun
and the smell of things being broken open
in the basement. Old friends I'd even had
crushes on, years & years ago
and now we sip on Cokes between paragraphs
of gossip, hearing distinct swishes
of an old proprietary ghost behind the curtain,
his collection of playbills long since faded &
bearing the fresh taboo of Clark Gable's
handsome grimace as he hauls Scarlett up the staircase
or blows cigar smoke over the glossy coiffure
of a Latin starlet – I don't know why
he came to mind, only that
I was once too romantic for my own good.

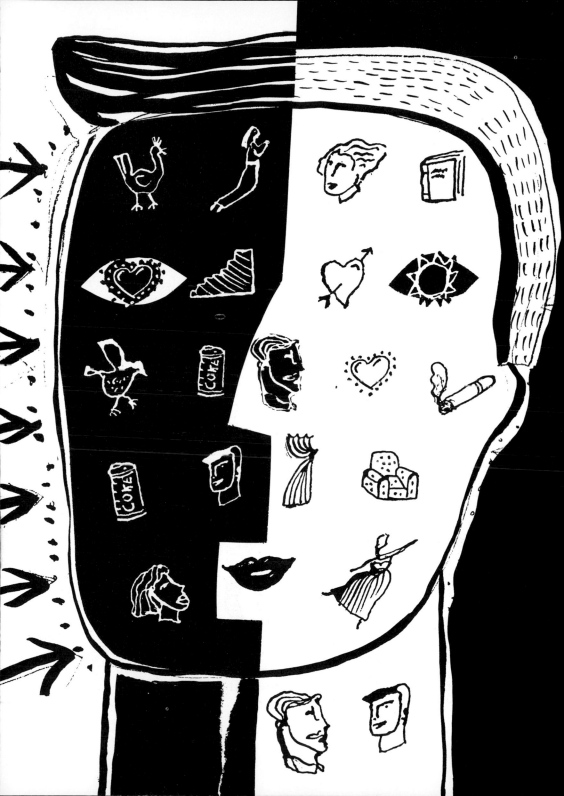

ALBERT WENDT
A Genealogy of Women

Another muggy summer night. It's been like this for days. Almost midnight. The heat clings to your skin, and every time you place your arms on the desk top, you leave sweatstains on it. The stains remind you of the bloodstains you left, as a boy, on the church steps where you fell and grazed your elbows. This is the third day of the Gulf War. Cocooned in your pain, you've not watched much of the twenty-four-hour television coverage of the War; it is a hygienic, clinical portrayal of the use and effectiveness of the latest weapons.

A large bushfly is sawing noisy holes in the still air around you. You're cauled in the orange light of the two lamps above your desk, and you're afraid to be born out of that light's safety, doing the only thing you have some gift for: letting your imagination, through this cheap ballpoint, wander to find its own levels and shapes of appropriateness. In the Trobriand Islands, the concept of genius is *sopi*, the ability of the creative imagination, like that of water, to search out and discover its own levels, without too much control or direction or the intellect's interference. For nights now, you've let your mind wander, searching to understand and contain the pain, the betrayal of twenty-six years when the woman you loved left.

The evening chorus of cicadas has stopped but their song still pulsates in your ears. Every evening when their chorus begins you remember that cicada which used to sit, at night, on your Grandmother Mele's gravestone outside your family home in the Vaipe, ticking, singing . . .

The door to sleep is closed.
Your thoughts strike that door and retreat.
Outside on your grandmother's grave
a lone cicada sucks up the night . . .

You used to suck in its song and nurse and savour it in the centre of your breath, making it part of your mythology.

You turn to the windows to your left. The reflection of the city's lights on the underbelly of the heavens filters into your study. The night is a white song. You imagine yourself inhaling it through your mouth. Inside you it grows like a gifted child. But it's not enough to dispel the pain and her memories and the *aitu* which accompany those memories . . .

Through the half-light you see the outline of Maungawhau's summit. Maungawhau is your mountain, your spiritual centre in this city. It lies gently on your chest when you're asleep, monitoring your dreams – and giving you the courage to face the evil *aitu* in your nightmares; it watches over you when you're awake, it sings to you when you're not well. Tonight you again feel the presence of the *atua* and *agaga* of the Tangata Maori, the original inhabitants of the mountain: they are extending their healing *mana* over your house and this city of black glass and business buildings that remind you of Darth Vader in a menacing mood.

Behind Maungawhau, standing in genealogical line, are your other spiritual mountains: Maungakiekie, Taranaki, Vaea who turned to stone while waiting for his beloved Apaula to return . . .

Mountains wouldn't be
mountains without the valleys ravines
and sea-level they rise up from.

They are
the rising high of sight propped up by stone
earth and sky.
They can't be
any other thing (and they know it).

They are
the eyes of earth gazing out,
gazing inwards, contemplating the future
on the horizon line and in the depths
of the whirling retina.

These mountains are
locked arm to arm, blood to blood,
and live in one another's thoughts . . .

You are suddenly aware that this house, your second skin, is humming absent-mindedly as it scrutinises you for signs and omens of your bitter grief. Your daughter Sina, her husband John, and your six-month-old granddaughter, Isabella Meleane, the new love of your life, are asleep in the next rooms. Since they came almost two months ago to live with you, they've filled your *moa*, your centre, with *alofa/aroha*, which has helped you combat the persistent *aitu* and memories. You try not to believe she's trampled on your *mana*, pride and dignity. You try, as your *moa* knots up again with the *aitu*, to turn away from that but you can't. You now see the past twenty-six years through her betrayal. Everything is tainted by it. This afternoon, when Sina showed you the photographs of her wedding, you saw them through that betrayal, too. Every memory you turn to is the same . . .

   Almost a year ago, in this house, in your backyard, Sina and John married. A beautiful Tangata Maori friend married them. The people you love most were there: your wife and children. You later tried to capture your joy in this poem:

Summer Wedding
(for Sina and Johnny)

I sit in our backyard shade drinking
ice-cold beer and the sun suspended in it.
Every time I put down my glass
the emperor sun is reborn in the liquid –
an embryo cauled in fire, a Van Gogh
sunflower, the succulent yellow of *kina*.

Along the backfence a peach tree,
a gum tree, creepers and punga,
six cicadas: two in the peach,
three in the gum tree, one in the creepers,
I count them by their different songs.

All week my son and I have weeded
the flower beds, trimmed the hedges,
mowed the lawns, raked and swept,
watered the young *pohutukawa* we planted
after Christmas in the far corner of the yard.

Last night in my sleep the full moon
wore a necklace of *tabua* above
Maungawhau and our city of black glass.
Maungakiekie's face was a *moko*
of green fire (the volcanoes died long ago).

Our home and yard are as neat
as the cicadas' celebrating chorus
ready for Sina's wedding tomorrow.
I keep drinking the sun to that,
Sina ia manuia le lua aiga!

You now read even that poem through her betrayal.

Get up, walk, pace the circumference of the lamplight cast over the carpet. One step at a time. One step into your imagination as it searches for levels of understanding to ease and heal your pain. Measure the strength of the *aitu* which grip your *moa* . . . Step forward one step at a time.

Finally you break from the light's circle and go across the corridor into your granddaughter's room.

The desk light is on. You stand above her cot, she's covered up to her neck in a blue duvet. A shimmering film of light keeps flowing in waves across her face and head, making her appear more a fabulous creature of fairy-tale and myth than fact. You want to reach down and cup your hands around her head, but you don't, afraid she may not be real. She loves bright reds, crimsons and scarlets. You know because she is mesmerised by those colours whenever you walk her round the garden. So you imagine her dreaming of all the large scarlet and crimson flowers in your garden and the world. You enter her dreaming and, through her, you relink to the three women who shaped the tongue of your imagination and the stories which are the mythology of your life.

Luisa Patu, your mother:

. . . memories of her are flamboyant
blooms scattered across
pitted lava fields under
the moon's scaffold or fish
darting among fabulous seaweed.
Escape from the grasp of my tongue,
images shatter into dust
from which myth rises . . .

Her father was Patu Togi, the Ali'i of Vaiala and a gentle and expert fisherman. Her grandfather was Asi Tunupopo, the notorious warrior leader who sold much of your district's lands to buy Papalagi weapons to fight his wars.

27

Your most lasting memory of your mother is of her playing her guitar and singing you to sleep with her lullabies. One of these songs weaves through your head tonight:

. . . sa ou ta'amilomilo i a'oaoga
ma lo'u loto ua tumu i le alofa.
Fia vaaia oe, Fa'ailoa,
o lo'o fa'amuli mai Samoa.
La'u pele, ua e polepole vale,
Ua e tu, i le uta a le vale,
Ua e le onosa'i ma e fa'apalepale,
O lou tofi ita mai le lagi . . .

Your mother's singing holds the night's *aitu* at bay, her plucking guitar resurrects a lover pining for a lost love. Your *moa* still holds *aroha* for your wife, you have to admit that to yourself, as your mother's song thaws your bitterness.

Your father, an expert musician, met your mother at her village. He visited weekly to teach the church choir; your mother was a member of the choir. Later, one of your father's favourite jokes was that she fell in love with his choir-conducting and he with her guitar!

Last year, during a reception at Maota Samoa in Auckland, your eldest daughter was talking to a friend when one of your community's most respected elders came up to her and stood gazing into her face. Then he turned to you and asked, 'Is this your daughter?' You nodded. 'I thought so, she looks just like your mother,' he whispered, with tears in his eyes.

A week or so later, when you told one of your aunts about the incident, she laughed and said, 'That elder was in love with your mother but she chose your father. Jokingly, he keeps telling people that your mother was wasted on that *meauli!*'

When your mother was ill with cancer, your father brought her from Samoa to Auckland Hospital. No cure. She died at thirty-five when you were fourteen and attending that cold, puritanical boys' boarding school in the shadow of Mount Taranaki . . .

When you were a boy, whenever your parents scolded or beat you or you wanted favoured treatment because your parents had to share their *alofa* between nine of you, you jumped on a bus at Apia Market near your home and fled to stay in Malie Village, with Aunt Ita, your father's eldest sister.

Her spacious home was always full of relatives and children. She was a widower and her own children were grown up. Right from your first visit, you knew you had a special place in her affections. She announced it to everyone there: You were the cleverest child in your whole *aiga* and you were going to be the first degreed person in that *aiga*! Every time you did well at secular school and pastor's school, she praised you loudly in front of your *aiga*. When you were thirteen and won a government scholarship to study in New Zealand, she assembled your *aiga* in Malie and conducted a *lotu*, thanking the Almighty for your exceptional achievement! Every three years when you returned from New Zealand for the Christmas vacations you had to give her some of your school photographs and certificates. The walls of her large sitting-room formed a gallery of family photographs; your photographs and certificates occupied a central place.

When you returned with your degree, she wept, and announced it to the whole village.

She kept you by her side whenever you stayed with her, telling you in detail your *aiga*'s genealogies and history, the connections of your *aiga* and Malie to other *aiga* and other villages – and it was all aristocratic – the latest information (gossip) about the internal politics of your *aiga*, and all the elaborate stories about her life. 'One day you must write it all down,' she kept telling you. And you have, you have, in poetry, story and novel, and in your own way.

When you refused to return to Apia and your parents, your parents used to visit Malie on the pretext of seeing how Aunt Ita was, and, while your father distracted Aunt Ita with non-stop conversation, your mother pleaded with you to return home with them. One time she even bribed you with the promise of a ticket to the latest Tarzan film at the Tivoli Theatre.

As time passed, Aunt Ita's children and the relatives who cared for her scattered, many migrating to New Zealand, Hawaii and America. So that in her last years she lived alone, with one or two nieces caring for her. She refused to shift and live with any of her children in Samoa or abroad. They sent her lots of money, had her house enlarged and renovated, and filled it with all the mod cons a middle-class mother might want: colour TV, electric stove, refrigerator, telephone . . .

You visited her for the last time in January 1988 before you and your family left for Auckland and your new job.

Aunt Ita was sitting in a wheelchair, fanning herself with a handfan, gazing into the past. A young niece was preparing her meal. She appeared a frail question mark occupying a doorway. She heard your footsteps on the back steps and turned. When she saw you, your wife, and children, she burst into a muted wailing. You embraced. She steadied. Welcomed you.

And so you talked the afternoon away. About your lives: your children's, your wife's, her life and ailments and memories and more memories. She joked to your children about the mischief you used to get up to as a boy; she again told them to grow up and be like you.

It was a joyous yet sad time. Sad because you knew you'd never see her again, alive.

As you remember her, those memories too are tainted by your wife's departure.

Aunt Ita died in October 1989. You and your wife were committed to going to Honolulu. You were a judge in the annual film festival there. You didn't go to her funeral in Samoa. You should have, you knew that as soon as your plane lifted off from Auckland Airport for Honolulu . . . You knew. Since then the guilt of not attending a beloved elder's funeral has squatted in your *moa* like an *aitu* you must appease.

Soon you must return to her grave in Malie and ask for her forgiveness.

You reach down and caress Isabella's cheeks and forehead, turn and return to your desk and the safety of the desk lights, pick up your ballpoint and continue scratching 'meanings' into the silence.

So tonight, without meaning to, your imagination has traced the levels and shapes of the female line of your genealogy, and now you're at the *moa* of that genealogy: Mele Tuaopepe, your father's mother, and the greatest storyteller you've ever known.

As you reinvent Mele, she returns and sits on your right shoulder, reading what you are writing. She sits cross-legged, hands clasped in her lap, head bowed, shrouded in her white sleeping sheet in that pose which she assumed at dawn, each day, when she woke and, as the sun broke over the eastern range, she started singing a hymn and your whole *aiga* – whether they wanted to or not – had to wake up and join her in your morning *lotu*. (Pity anyone who didn't: she threw her hard *ali* at that person!) Her white sheet in the gleaming light of morning took on the luminosity of white fire, offsetting the dark ebony sheen of her skin. As a child, you saw her as an ageless creator-being who would never die.

Mele's mother was of the aristocratic *aiga* Sa-Malietoa of Sapapaalii; her father was the British Consul. She didn't discuss this latter side of her family much. She was raised mainly in her Samoan *aiga* in the Faa-Samoa. Because she was the eldest child (and the brightest, she used to boast, and Mele was arrogant!), the elders in our *aiga* made her the keeper and guardian of our genealogies, land, history, knowledge and stories. Through her British side, she inherited the English language – a guttural tongue, she accused it of

30

being – and the whole heritage of knowledge and literature in English. By the age of twenty-five (why twenty-five, she never explained) she'd memorised the Bible, she told us. She'd also read all the books in English in her father's library. So hers was the richest storehouse of mythologies you'd ever known. (You can't help but feel that she also persuaded you to believe that!)

When she was 'young and very beautiful' (her description: there was a portrait of her in your father's house to attest to that beauty) she married your father's father. 'The handsomest young German in Samoa,' she told you children. (He was mainly Samoan, the grandson of Maualaivao, the Alii of Malie.) Years ago you tried to snare him and his history this way:

My grandfather –
and I can only describe him from
a photograph cobwebbed in my
father's cupboard – died
too of whisky, at thirty-six.
'Tall, dark and handsome' is apt
for him. No glass eye for
this Hollywood trader marooned
Arrogant gleam in his eyes
    with nowhere to sail
    without a ship,
straight junker nose inhaling
    the bitter serenity
    of failure.
Thick Polynesian lips shaped
    for wine, whisky
    and fierce infidelities.
White-suited in a cane chair,
the Kaiser of Whisky come courting
the camera, in love with Bismarck,
burdened with the failure of Europe,
heir to the cold crystal eye.

They had six children, your father was the third eldest.

She remarried Tuaopepe Tauilo, of the *aiga* Sa-Tuala of Lefaga. That is another saga you must one day write.

So when you were born, you were born into her world as a grandmother and the matriarch of your *aiga*, into her storehouse of story, myth, poetry, song, history, English, Samoan, a bit of German, legends, fairy-tales, and their infinite possibilities and combinations. She took the traditional ways of telling and reinvented them to suit the changes the Papalagi had brought.

Every evening when you were children, while you lay in your mosquito nets, she enriched your imaginations with her stories, told the Fagogo way, *her* way.

Traditional myths, legends, stories, poetry, nursery rhymes, jingles, *tupua*, Greek mythology, Christian mythology, *Grimms' Fairy-Tales*, *Aesop's Fables*, *The Iliad*, *The Adventures of Sinbad the Sailor*, *Gunga Din*, *Treasure Island*, etc. Because she told these 'foreign' stories the Fagogo way and in Samoan, you believed them to be *her* stories, the stories of Samoa. It wasn't until you went to boarding school in New Zealand and read the actual books that you knew otherwise. But her telling, you found, was more compelling and exciting than the books themselves.

Usually you had to work for her stories. While she lay under her blanket, on her side, her head resting on her *ali*, a group of you had to *lomi* her legs or pound her back lightly with your fists. To ensure you all stayed awake, she used the Fagogo technique of the Tagi to do so. Each Fagogo has a Tagi, a chorus, which the teller teaches her audience. During the telling, the teller, if she suspects her audience may be falling asleep, would suddenly stop the story and say, 'Tagi mai le tatou Fagogo!' Meaning, 'Recite to me the chorus of our Fagogo!' And you have to recite it. 'Louder!' she'd call if she felt you were not awake fully!

Not once do you remember Mele falling asleep during her telling.

When you were about ten, she and Aunt Ita and a group of relatives took you to the island of Savai'i to revisit her *aiga* in different villages. Why she took you out of all her grandchildren, you've never figured out. On that visit you trekked across the awesome beauty of the lava fields . . .

The lava spreads for miles right into the sea. Nothing else. Just black silence like the moon maybe . . . A flood of lava everywhere. But in some places you see small plants growing through the cracks in the lava, like funny stories breaking through your stony mind. Get me? I felt like I have been searching for that all my miserable life . . . That we are all equal in the silence, in the nothing, in lava. I did not want to leave the lava fields, but . . . then you cannot stay there for ever because you will die of thirst and hunger if you stay. There is no water, no food, just lava. All is lava!

She and Aunt Ita made the history and mythology of place and your *aiga* come alive, as you moved from village to village, discovering the *alofa* and *faaaloalo* of *aiga* and community.

You also absorbed into yourself the long sad silence of the rainforest.

Mele was small, physically, and grew smaller as she aged. But she was huge in presence and vanity. She refused to be called an *olomatua*, an old woman. Even during large public functions she chastised anyone, including the highest ranking *alii*, who called her that.

Whenever the *matai* and other elders of your *aiga* met to discuss family affairs, she didn't attend those meetings, but all the important decisions had to be reported to her. (Sometimes, she sent some of the older children to listen and report back to her.) If she disagreed with any decision, she told your father, who was the head of your *aiga*, to reconsider it or call another meeting. Because she knew all the *gafa*, history and land boundaries, everyone in your *aiga* *needed* her: she provided the information for *matai* title and land disputes, the detailed stories to substantiate any of your *aiga*'s claims to those. She also knew the skeletons in the histories of the elders in your *aiga* and villages and sometimes used those to frighten them into line. She was pleasant about it though. She never did it for herself, it was to protect and strengthen your *aiga*. She was also loved because of her boundless generosity which your father and everyone in your *aiga* had to provide the means for. Almost everything she acquired or was given she gave to those who needed it and to her church.

She refused to live in a Papalagi house. When she was in her eighties and your *aiga* was living in the Vaipe, Apia, your father built a large house and asked her to move into it. She never did. She continued living in your Samoan *fale*, where, every evening, you and the other children went to sleep beside her. She refused to have chairs, beds and other Papalagi furniture in her *fale*.

She also refused to take any Papalagi medicine. During national health campaigns she was polite to the health workers who came round with whatever health cure had to be taken by the population. She sometimes astonished the medical workers with her knowledge of Papalagi medicine, promised faithfully she would take her prescribed dose, but, as soon as the paramedics left, she threw the medicine out of her *fale*, and told you not to trust such alien cures. Her cure for ill-health was hard manual work, gardening and weeding especially. She also had two friends who were well-known *fofo*, healers. Two large, huggable women who came, with their herbal-massage and other cures, whenever Mele summoned them. You loved listening to the three of them, slurping their Samoan cocoa, munching their cabin bread and cheese and tinned salmon – Mele's favourite food – and gossiping conspiratorially about your neighbourhood and country.

In the late-sixties she became addicted to one Papalagi invention, television. Your father was the first in the Vaipe to get a set, and your house was crowded every evening with people from the neighbourhood. Because Mele's great-grandchildren wanted to see TV, she had to bring them from her *fale* to the house. At first, she used to fall asleep early as she watched the TV. Then you began to notice how attentive she was becoming to *Bonanza, Sesame Street, I spy, Star Trek*, etc. Many of the features of those programmes became part of her stories.

Like Aunt Ita, she too watched generations of your *aiga* growing up and migrating abroad. She was sorrowful with every departure. To her death, she always had one or two great-grandchildren to bring up in her *fale*, though.

The night before you were to leave for New Zealand on a scholarship, she sent the other children away to the Papalagi house and asked you to stay. She patted the mat beside her. You went and sat there. She blew out the kerosene lamp and, in the darkness, she placed her right hand over your head. 'Some day you too will be a special teller,' she blessed you. 'But with it will come pain, for to tell the stories of life well, you'll have to know suffering, you'll even have to experience a taste of death, a momentary death of the *agaga*, repeatedly. But the *atua* will be merciful . . .'

Since your wife left, you have once again experienced that death . . .

Tonight as you turn and gaze into Mele's eyes, you want to drown in them, drift down into her depths and just be suspended in her amniotic tide. But she won't let you. She insists you continue being a witness to the suffering and *alofa*, capturing them in the gift of language she gave to you.

She died at ninety-three or ninety-four: she didn't know her exact birthday. After an argument with your father, her favourite child, she left, angrily, for Malie, to stay with Aunt Ita who was jealous of the favouritism Mele had always shown for your father. While there, she got angry with one of the great-grandchildren and while chasing the child with a *salu*, she fell and dislocated her hip. To Aunt Ita's bitter disappointment, Mele insisted on being brought back to her favourite son's house.

Her *fofo* friends put her hip back into place, but she couldn't walk. The elders of your *aiga* gathered; she told them she had decided her life was over and wanted them to prepare her grave under her favourite breadfruit tree just outside the house. Your father and the other men of your *aiga* carried out her instructions. During that time, hundreds of relatives and friends arrived, from all over Samoa, to say goodbye to her.

The elders of your *aiga* never talked about Mele's youngest sister. Not by name anyway. They referred to her, in hushed tones, as 'Mele's youngest sister'. You'd always wondered why they were afraid of her, of someone you'd not seen.

It was mid-morning; you remember the white heat of the sun on the lawns and the roof of the house, the expectant stillness. You were sitting cross-legged on the edge of the *fale*; your aunts and two other women sat round Mele who was lying, covered with her favourite blanket, on a bed of mats. You all turned to look at the main road together.

A short woman with brilliant white hair, in grey blouse and black *lavalava*, and sheltering under a black umbrella, was approaching. In the heat waves shimmering up from the earth, she appeared to be floating a few inches above the ground. 'She is here,' Aunt Mine announced. Mele nodded. Who? you asked yourself. 'It has been a long time,' Mele said.

As the woman neared us, Aunt Mine and the other women withdrew respectfully from Mele's *fale*. You wondered why, and felt uncomfortable.

White-haired, yet the face was very young, unlined and wonderfully serene. She stopped, lowered her umbrella and came up the front steps. She didn't look at you.

She knelt down beside Mele who was gazing up at her. 'Have you come?' Mele greeted her, reaching up with both arms. 'Yes, my sister,' the woman replied, reaching forward. Deep muted wailing from the depths of the *moa*, as they embraced for a long time. 'It has been a long time, Mele,' the woman said, sitting back. Mele nodded. You felt an intruder and retreated to the kitchen of the house, finding everyone's attention was on Mele and her visitor.

'Who is she?' you asked. The elders avoided the question.

'Mele's youngest sister,' Aunt Mine replied. You waited for her name and her history. None was given. 'Where is she from?' you persisted. The elders looked apprehensive.

'She is the Guardian of the Sauma'iafe,' your father admitted finally. 'She is a renowned *taulasea* who heals *ma'i aitu*.' The Sauma'iafe was once a powerful pre-Christian *atua*. The missionaries and Christians had outlawed Her, turning Her into an evil *aitu* to be feared. As her Guardian and a healer of diseases caused by *aitu*, Mele's sister was to be feared as a pagan force from the Days-Before-the-Coming-of-the-Light. You goose-pimpled with awe and admiration, as you watched the woman.

They talked for a long time. No one dared interrupt them. The Guardian left at noon.

The next morning, Aunt Mine sat with Mele and listed down all of Mele's direct descendants. They totalled a hundred. Your second child, who your wife was carrying at the time, was the hundredth. When she was born a few months later, you named her Mele.

At mid-morning – there was a refreshing breeze sweeping through the *fale* and the sugar cane behind it – the elders assembled round Mele. She told your father she wanted to look at her grave. He picked her up and, carrying her in his arms, took her to it. He walked with her around the open grave which was covered with fine *siapo*, while you watched from the *fale*.

When they returned and your father placed her in her bed of mats, she told your *aiga* that it was a good and apt place.

She died that night.

Throughout your life, you have viewed the whole drama of her dying as her last grand story, planned and executed with nobility and style befitting the life of the grand storyteller and matriarch.

Out of the top drawer of your desk you take out the thick manuscript of the unfinished novel you've been writing over the past fifteen years. A novel which tries to measure and capture the inventive dimensions and style of her life, and in which her sister, the Guardian of the Sauma'iafe, who you only saw once, appears as major character and force. Mele appears as Peleiupu.

You open the first page and read:

> During the final moments of her dying, ninety-nine years later, Peleiupu (or Pele, as nearly everyone came to call her) was to remember, in slow vivid detail, that incredible dawn when her father, Mautu Tuifolau, pressed a dew-covered mango against her left cheek and she was instantly pierced down to her tingling toes with the sharp cold kiss of it; and, at that startled moment, she was conscious, for the first time, that she was an entity (I, me) separate from everything else . . .

Isabella's muffled crying breaks into your reading. You hear Sina get up to go to her. You look up at the windows. The lead-grey light of dawn is seeping through them. You shut the manuscript.

The mugginess has lifted.

You rise from your desk and go to the windows. Your skin turns a mercury brightness in the strengthening light. The summit of Maungawhau is outlined in the dawn sky.

'We are the thread we plait across the abyss of all that we've forgotten,' Mele whispers. 'You live in your children and Isabella and the thread that stretches back through your mother, Aunt Ita, me, and, for generation upon generation, to Tagaloaalagi, our Supreme Atua.'

You think of Falealupo, Land's End at the western tip of Savai'i, and the Fafa, the lava tunnel which the *agaga* of the Dead depart from for Pulotu, the Spirit World.

In her low muted voice, Mele starts chanting the Genesis which she taught you when you were a boy. You join her chanting. Your chant gives birth to the world, again, while the Gulf War continues on TV:

Tagaloaalagi, the Supreme Atua, lives in the Vanimonimo (Disappearing space between). He created all things, only He without *lagi* (sky) or *lauele'ele* (land), only He wandering in the Vanimonimo, without *sami* (sea) also or *nu'u* (countries), and where He stood the *papa* (rock) grew up.

Tagaloafa'atutupunu'u (Tagaloa, creator of countries) was His name also.

And Tagaloa said to the rock, split now and Papataoto (rock that lies) was born . . .

JENNY BORNHOLDT
Overseas

For years she has listened to people talk about overseas. For years, over dinner, someone has been saying *St Peter's Square* and everyone at the table has nodded. After some years she also began to nod because the Square and other places had become so familiar she felt she had been there. She could now recount her own stories of overseas. When someone said, 'that café in Paris, the one painted red inside, to the left of the Arc de Triomphe,' she could chip in, with all confidence, saying, 'no, no, it's on the right, two down from the place that sells the wonderful bagels.'

*   *   *

She has an aunt who cuts plastic New World Supermarket bags into strips and knits them into sunhats with large brims. Once she made her husband – now dead – a hat from Coca Cola cans opened out, with the edges crocheted together in red wool.
This same aunt has a fondness for old Sunlight Liquid containers – the large ones. She cuts the top three-quarters of the fronts out and constructs nativity scenes inside with Mary, Joseph, Baby Jesus and the Three Wise Men in their yellow manger.

Would this happen in Paris?
                    Or Rome?

*   *   *

In Wellington she can buy coffee and have it ground in a machine called CLIMAX.

*   *   *

In Pomplona in Spain they run with the bulls. She knows this from reading James A. Michener.
Her sixty-year-old aunt once wrestled a huge bull over a fence after it had gored her husband. Her advice, after further reading on the subject, is:

If you are being charged by a bull, don't run,
and don't eyeball it. Stand side on so you don't
appear as a large obstacle.

*   *   *

Photos from America

Here's Phil, Nick, me, Susie, Guy and Steve,

and this is Randy, Gary, me, Susie, Bud and Jolene eating tacos in Mexico.

*   *   *

Violet – her grandmother – writes to her from Greymouth. She sends
photographs of old movie stars saying they are photographs of her in her
younger days. Here is a picture of me and here is a picture of my first
husband Jeremiah. He was a dashing young man with a temper as quick
as a rattlesnake, she says of Clark Gable. I left him after he gambled
away all our money. After that I went on a long journey where I ended up
doing acrobatics on the back of a horse in a circus in Madrid. It was after I
returned home that I met your grandfather who was a true gentleman and
never did me wrong.

Here is a picture of a man I met in Madrid. We had what you young
people would call a 'wild time'. The music, the dancing, the wine, the
starry nights . . . Oh, it makes me weep to remember.

Here are the gardens in Paris where my first husband Jean-Paul proposed
to me, writes Violet. He was very handsome and he gave me a rose.
Alas, our life together was cut tragically short when he was drowned in
a boating accident. I felt robbed of love. It was then that I decided it was
dangerous to marry foreigners. They die and leave you in ways you are
unaccustomed to.

*   *   *

In a bookshop in the central city a man orders books on the Beatles:

> The Beatles in Tokyo
> The Beatles in Holland
> Dark Horse: Secret Life of George Harrison

and   *Four Ever – Die Geschichte Beatles*, in which the text is in German but the pictures are in English.

*   *   *

She reads in an overseas magazine:

> The Shopping Bag is the tip
> of the iceberg . . . the essence of
> image . . . the haiku.

So this is how they view it over there. Writing as carrier bag. The poem as shopping trundler. The short story as overnight bag. The novel a leather suitcase with wheels for ease of movement.

*   *   *

She knows that all young French women are tall, thin and have short black hair. They are independent and wear white cotton underpants which come up to their waist.

When they become older they are still thin but their hair is long and blonde and pulled up into a sophisticated yet casual roll at the back. They have a husband who knows about cooking and two beautiful children, yet they are often disappointed.

*   *   *

Her cousin bought the New York State and the Chrysler Buildings in Wellington, years ago.
The Chrysler Building he assembled in Wellington but it was recently moved up the coast to Waikanae.
The New York State he made one cold winter in Tokyo and now it's in London in the main room of his Kensington apartment. It's lit up at

night and you have to be careful not to knock it over as you go through the door.

*   *   *

Because she is alone she is almost as popular as Michelangelo's *David*. Families all over the world have her in their holiday snaps. She just seems to get in the way, the only one not smiling, looking away.

I was sure we only had three children, couples say to each other. Who is this? friends of families all over the world ask. Oh, that's just someone we met, they say: my sister's stepdaughter from her husband's third marriage, the mother of Brian's illegitimate children. That, they say, is the daughter we never had. We found her in Florence and she recognised us instantly.

The Bathers
Les Grandes Baigneuses – Cézanne
(begun about 1898 or 1899 and finished 1905)

Left for eight years amidst
the intense green and blue
of trees   pleased Cézanne
abandoned them in such a
pleasurable landscape.
Bodies slanted towards trees,
water, a dog asleep on the
ground. They sighed, over those
eight years, talked amongst
themselves quietly, each morning
a small *ah* of pleasure
at the day, wondering if
today . . . for eight years
until the trees grew thick
with colour, the lake
darkened and their bodies'
cool formation fixed
beside the admiring water.

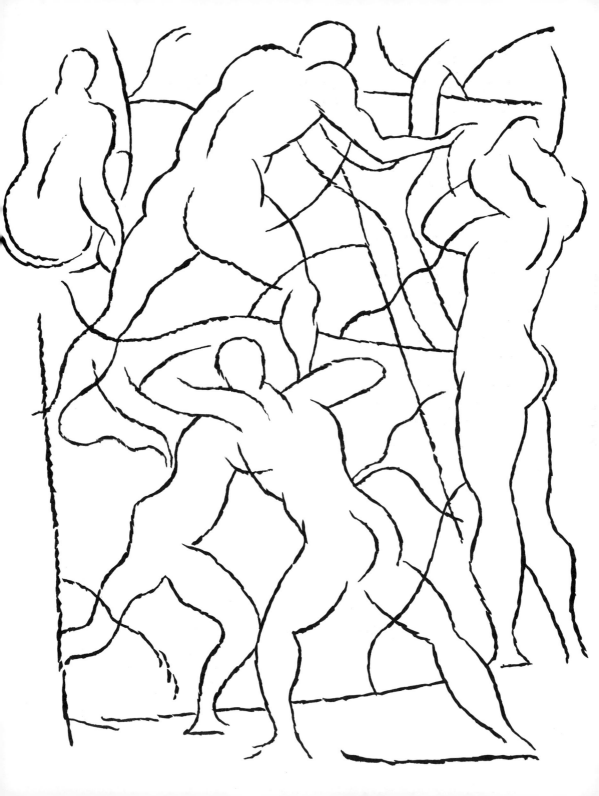

VINCENT O'SULLIVAN
Hund, Fuchs und Katze
(Franz Marc, 1888–1916)

Placid on arcs of colour, contained in themselves,
white hound, grey cat, rust-coloured fox,
in paradisal arrangement, nineteen hundred and twelve:
the hound flexes a casual paw,
the cat may just have been fed, the fox
sleeps solid as only dream-foxes may.
The one intrusive colour, not in mind or flesh,
is that wedge of metallic blue, a polished rim
of something not yet focused, horizon-
heavy, which the pale hound hasn't yet a whiff
of, nor the cat snugly grey in self-reflection,
nor the somnolent fox whose nature is to spot
the difference. Franz Marc is touching deftly
the rondures of life with the crescents
of design, he is flaring the world more
vivid in its shapely facts.
                        Ach, to leave
such things as they are, *die schönen Dinge*!
– the dull snore of the fox from brush to snout,
the chalky canine leg and the lowered head,
the cat which is fat as history at that tick
of the clock.
                        He shall come back to that blue
in say four years' time. It shall spread wider
then, edge decidedly deeper, shine so quickly
it leaps into pure chance. Fuchs and Katze
and Hund shall never know it. For Franz
has used it completely, walked away with the lot.
Into the blue and out of it, together.

PHILIP DAVISON
The Fishmonger

Next time take a close look at that fishmonger, but don't linger. He sits at the door of his fish shop on a chair that doesn't have a back to it. He's got this wrap of white hair and a thin sweep over the bald dome. He's got big ears; he can use them like gills to breathe. When he's finished painting prices on the window he sits on that chair looking like a fish, and that's uncommon. A lot has to do with his expression. It must, mustn't it? Bridie, his wife, she's behind the counter. There's just the two of them. They had a girl for a while, but that didn't work out. She wasn't happy. That was fifteen years ago. Maybe more. After the girl, he wouldn't employ anyone else. Now, they couldn't have anyone else even if they wanted. They couldn't pay. Not enough to satisfy. An island race that doesn't eat fish, he says. So, the fish man sits at the door with his slack mouth closed, with bus fumes in his nostrils. Bridie looks out the window from the back of the shop. He allows for this in his painting of prices on the glass. In a decade, virtually no money has been spent on the place, but it is kept clean and the fish is always fresh. The fishmonger and his wife are old, sedentary, but sharp-witted. They're there to sell fish and spend themselves on whoever is willing to converse. Everything else is as it is – an island race that doesn't eat fish; as they have made it – fresh cod £1.80 per lb; as they let it be – gold wedding anniversary tomorrow.

The fishmonger had asked that the regular poker meeting be brought forward one night. He explained and the three other players wished him well. A polite enquiry followed as to how the event was to be celebrated. Collective good wishes to be conveyed to the wife. Nothing more. No dull wit. For that the fishmonger was grateful. He wanted only to play poker, to drink, to smoke and talk as they did on other poker nights, with rueful, jocular arrogance.

The players thickened in their dark suits when they set their heavy bones on the dining-room chairs. In the draper's house the game was played in the bay window of the upstairs parlour. The draper's grandson liked to watch. He sniggered at the fishmonger for being a fishmonger. He pulled faces at the fish-shop window. Sniggered with his friends on the corner like they'd been asked to do it. The little bastard was delighted to see the fishmonger lose with his first hand of cards.

'This car that you bought,' said the bookie. 'Will it last?'

'It'll survive us all,' replied the draper.

'I had a look at it,' said the plumber.

'Well?' enquired the fishmonger. 'Is it a heap of junk, or what?'

'You'll be the first to go,' interjected the draper.

'It'll last a while,' said the plumber flatly.

'Is it for Nora?' the fishmonger asked.

'Not at all. Not with her eyes. She's no desire for a car.'

'What do you want with a second-hand car? Haven't you bags of money for a new car?'

Bags of money was a sore point with the draper. Bags of money was a running joke. The others chortled.

'And what's wrong with the car you have?' asked the bookie.

'I'll be fixing this one up and selling it.'

'So it *is* a heap of junk.'

'Deal the cards.'

'A heap of junk, eh? Sure who'll buy a wreck except somebody like yourself and you wouldn't have bought it if it hadn't been a knockdown price. You've been hoodwinked. Those second-hand car dealer fellas are blackguards.'

'Never mind the car, willya? Just deal the cards.'

They played poker. The fishmonger lost heavily, far more than he should have wagered, more than the others should have allowed, more than anyone had lost in this longstanding weekly game. The draper won most of it. They all saw the fishmonger curl his lip to stop his jaw from trembling. His three friends, unwittingly in league, were greatly discomfited.

'Golden anniversary, you say?' blurted the bookie. 'I admit there are times I regret not having married. For the comfort of it. Having a woman to listen out for you. It's selfish, I know . . .'

'Let's break for a drink, shall we?' said the draper. 'A celebratory drink. We ought to be ashamed of ourselves for not having raised our glasses to our dear friend's happiness.'

'Yes,' agreed the plumber heartily, jumping to his feet to fill their glasses. 'We're mugs for not having raised a toast . . .'

Suddenly, all but the fishmonger were up off their chairs, standing somewhat stooped in their creased suits. 'What sort of friends are we, not thinking to raise our glasses?'

'Please,' said the fishmonger, 'I'd rather we just continued.'

'Nonsense. Hold out your glass.'

'No, please.' He had lost the money he had set aside for the following night, for the dinner with Bridie.

On the last game there was a very large pot. It seemed appropriate – a way of mocking the tension, of making light of the fishmonger's misfortune – to allow so much to ride on one bet to which the fishmonger was not party. It was between the draper and the bookie. The draper lost all he had accumulated to the bookie. The draper got up from the table and joined the fishmonger at the window. They both looked waxily into a black sky. The bookie was embarrassed by the sum of money he had won. Nothing could be done, however, except confirm that the poker school would meet on the regular night next week in the bookie's kitchen.

This anniversary, it fell on one of those sunny days. People in hot climates don't know what that kind of day is like. Sun beating on the fishmonger's street. The fishmonger sweating at the door. Sun beating on his dry aquarium. Fish in ranks on the marble. Bridie in the cool of the shop, lost. 'I Dreamt that I Dwelt in Marble Halls' she would sing when she'd be standing to sing.

Today, there were fewer customers than usual. Bridie patiently kept watch. The fishmonger sat, legs apart, feet pressed flat on to the pavement, slack mouth closed but lip curled. Suddenly, he rose from his chair and announced to Bridie that he had a message to do. He removed his apron and white coat, put on his suit jacket and deserted his post. Bridie loathed being left in the shop by herself. Equally, she loathed being in their house by herself, though this was rare now. She was content with him in the next room or in bed above her, close enough so that he would hear her if she called, though she never did call.

The fishmonger moved slowly along the pavement, more slowly than usual because of the heat. His selling fish was comparable to playing poker with a bookie, he thought. Yes, that was it. Time to give it up. He had no sentimental attachment to fish. He would ask that fool of an accountant what the business was worth. Do it properly. The fishmonger heard sniggers as he entered the bank, but ignored them.

When he returned to the shop he found Bridie singing softly to herself. She was sure he had remembered their anniversary. However, the old man said nothing, and he had not brought back a parcel or package. Perhaps he had something in his pocket. Something small. Bridie had something for him. She had left it on the mantelpiece. A gold tie-pin and cuff links with his initials engraved.

Now that Bridie was serving a customer, the fishmonger noticed that the singing had stopped. He couldn't remember when she had last sung like that. Why didn't she sing more often? Sundays, when the shop was closed, they were the worst. Why didn't she sing on Sundays? She had had lessons as a child. Why had nothing come of her singing? The fishmonger was distracted by a simple click, the click of a camera shutter. He had just been photographed by a young man with an expensive camera not ten feet away. Most disturbing. The old man rose from his chair.

'Here, what are you at? What do you think you're doing, sonny?'

The young man took two more photographs. 'You don't mind, do you?'

The fishmonger went berserk. He threw his bulk behind the delivery of a blow that sent the young man spinning into the roadway where he landed on his back on the oily mess created by the buses. 'Do I mind? Do I what?' He wrenched the camera from the dazed man, opened the back of it, pulled out the film from its cartridge. 'What do you want my picture for?' he bellowed. 'Make fools of people, would you? You should learn to leave people in peace.' He was now standing over the young man, camera raised above his head.

'Your face . . . just your face . . . in this light.' The young man was terrified. He tried to get to his feet but was pummelled on his back. Bridie came running out of the shop in time to prevent her husband from braining the young man with the camera.

'Make a fool of me, eh?' said the fishmonger. With all his might he flung the camera to the ground. He pulled free of Bridie's hands, picked up the film and tried to eat it.

Now the fishmonger was choking and he had cut his gums on the Celluloid. The young man scrambled backwards on the greasy road. He managed to get to his feet. There were people watching. From a safe distance the young man protested about the damage to himself and his camera. He threatened to call the police. Bridie brought her choking husband into the shop and bolted the door behind them. The customer who was being served at the time of the extraordinary occurrence had been watching through Bridie's portion of window. He was a regular customer, a newspaper man from across the street. He unbolted the door and retrieved the fishmonger's chair and sat the old man on it with his back to the tiled wall while Bridie went for a cup of water.

'Dear God,' she cried. 'What's happened? What came over him?'

'It's all right,' said the newspaper man. 'He'll be all right.'

The fishmonger had calmed somewhat. Suddenly, he was exhausted and frail. His mouth was bleeding inside, but he kept it shut.

The newspaper man returned to the shop an hour later with a newspaper photographer. This photographer wasn't like the last one. He was stout, middle aged, dying of nicotine-induced cancer. He held out his hand when he was introduced to the fishmonger. The newspaper man had told the fishmonger that he wanted to write a story on him – one of a dwindling band of city-centre traders, a true Dubliner, a proud man under siege – and would he mind having his photograph taken outside his shop? The fishmonger agreed. He posed outside his fish shop with a set mouth and didn't blink. They wanted him on his chair, but he insisted on standing. Bridie closed the shop as soon as the newspaper men had left.

He had no present for her, but he had arranged to take her to dinner at the Shelbourne Hotel. He dressed in his best suit and wore his new tie-pin and cuff links. Secretly, he was embarrassed to have his initials displayed, but what of it? There were the events of the afternoon to bear. Bridie had said nothing of it all since they left the shop. She spent an extraordinary length of time getting ready. They were both anxious that the night should set things right for them. After all, there was just the two of them. The old man needed help. She needed reassurance, some measure of her worth.

It was a splendid dinner with champagne. She was determinedly flushed with pleasure. Though his stomach wasn't right, he ate most of what was put in front of him. He swilled his champagne about his pained gums. He kissed her in public – awkwardly, when they were waiting for their coats. She couldn't remember the last time he had kissed her in public. He was making up for having denied her at the poker game in the draper's house.

They stepped out into the street, into the cold night air, the steadier for their confirmatory dinner. Outside the hotel they bought a newspaper, the late-evening edition. There was a small item and a photograph. The headline read: FISH MAN LASHES OUT. There was the photograph of the fishmonger standing outside his shop. This man, it ran, is yet another elderly victim of the misdirected urban plan that leaves our inner cities a hunting-ground for marauding youths of a remarkable diversity. This is one man who has made a stand. It went on to recount how, on being abused and harried by a cheeky amateur photographer, the old man finally resorted to physical force to remove the offender. It quoted the fishmonger as having said that his shop was no museum, that he was there to sell fish and hadn't time for an insolent young pup with a camera, that the youth of today needed to learn manners.

The fishmonger looked to his wife. 'Did I say those things?' he asked with a heavy heart.

'It's talk,' Bridie said, linking arms with him, 'just talk.'

The fishmonger chose to sit with his wife for all that was left of their waking hours that night, though they scarcely spoke. While she carefully cut out the picture of her husband from the newspaper, in another part of the city a young man with an aching back examined that same newspaper picture. It was astonishing to see it, that same face he had attempted to photograph hours earlier. Here it was, in the newspaper: FISH MAN LASHES OUT. His own portrait of the fish man would have been a stronger image, it would have been more revealing – the old man on his chair, his posture, his expression – but even this facile portrait of him standing in front of his shop with a hard grimace had something of the fish in it.

Terrified Australis

Terry Australis

GLYN MAXWELL
Two Poems
The Recording Time

I didn't dream this, hell.
On a waking day of twenty hours, no break
for sun, no bite outside, to make this reel
of film of what I'd seen so far and make
it true while beautiful,

the morning coughed away
between old hands insisting on one thing.
I had from the outset, a ringed fortuitous day
munching with ideas and unlimiting
time accorded me,

been boldly clear and sure
of the most painless splashing on a screen
what had been thought and worded only. 'Pure,'
I told them; 'pure.' They nodded and between
the console and the door

shook on it and left.
It does no good to raise it back to words
from film – that's picking milk up – it involved
a bloke in rainbow fog inside a woods,
a pond and a blue croft,

your inevitable garden –
to say it does no good; it was my effort
in a new city, optimistic, written
up and backed up, copied and delivered
and about to happen –

but through that afternoon,
that worked hunger, light, friendship and humour
to bony, minor matters in a room
the wires of which and cables led forever
somewhere, and where soon

time would be running out
always because it was never early, they said
again, the knowall men, that the work without
their 'one thing' (it was a girl, and it was sad
but what could be done?

it's how it is) would die
out in the market, 'However,' they paused: 'pure.'
But on we went, me bowed and getting my way
between their sighs and shrugs and mutters 'sure'
as time went eating by,

a reel of confidence
stolidly passing tape to a reel of fear,
while the yellow little Empire States of sounds
bobbed and fell in a row and the engineer
sampled his own silence.

They had a girl in mind.
Though I did too by now and not just one.
And they had more than one: the mixer found
a window for a few to catch the sun
eight seconds from the end;

another guy had snaps
of his brunette, and how the scarlet flowers
would set her off! another felt perhaps
his sisters should be extras. Ten hours
from either shore, the gaps

GLYN MAXWELL

in what we'd done so far
looked to be filling with the blonde and blue eye-
lidded loves of everyone in there
except for lone refusing you-know-who. I
kept to my wire chair,

experiencing hours
for what they are, staggeringly tough
when nothing but yourself can be called yours
and failure and vod look more like love
than do fame and flowers.

My place became a helm,
my flying hair the Dutchman's, and my words
curses on the orchestrated calm
of expert eyes and monitoring reds
piloting the room.

Later even than then,
I got to thinking of men, as the single man
I had created and could see ran on
through drenching lemon glades and fell and ran
up to a bannered throne –

but we were in the ground
ourselves and empty of impulse but to end
this day's work. I thought on a light land,
ideas changing there, an oncoming friend,
his open-to-me hand,

and then I jumped and saw
the engineers and mixers, and the two
who got me here and the luckless janitor
who never quits this complex glowing blue
and seated where they were

60

as if asleep, and I
in all the studio saw nothing red,
but everything hot blue like a late sky
had lowered at a given time and dyed
all in indigo dye.

I didn't dream that, no.
We were all done, they woke and there was drink,
much, and a toiling up, out to the low
reddening sun that still made us blink
as we began to go.

The tape I took was mine
to keep, a master, I walked the city, tense
with simmering delay, my advancing spine
setting up my foolery with its sense.
And I was fine with pain.

Home was as dark as when
you are not it, home, and the hall was first
of the ghosts to tell and ask me, 'Nothing, then.'
I sat down as I always do, as a guest,
especially when alone,

and the film flickered and ran . . .
They'd laced it with their girls to the sight's end.
I slumped back I myself the central man
before all possibilities, all kind
of seen, sipping woman,

and saw her glance or sigh,
wear little or lilac, silk or less and step
towards, away, and back to come to my
numb aid. It was an endless tape, a loop.
It blew out Sunday.

And Leaves Astonishing

G L Y N   M A X W E L L

For now, among the falling of the ochres,
Reds and yellows, in which haze the many
   Casualties of what on earth
Went on here this month, re-fuse, this joker's
Pockets open out and he digs for money.

His the face suggested to, spat on,
In which the door and final door were shut,
   The mother of which saw and lost
At stations, and the quizzes of the Western
Shows made to a shape you don't forget:

Human of the Revolution, soul
We would wouldn't we be if our dreams
   Loomed amateur ciné of tanks
Slowing round our corner and the whole
Hope thing holed and fumbling in own homes –

For now he buys and smokes and his rivered mug
Grins above the inhalation. It all
   Rustles by beyond him now,
The elbowing to run the show, the lag
Of bloody onus, economic stall,

The eloquence and begging in the States
And books of what it was, means, portends.
   Photographed and asked, he moves
His hand to – what, to offer cigarettes
Nobody takes. He takes and lights one, stands

And leaves, astonishing the siding rich
With just being. The love sticks on the tongue.
   He goes his way, who went his way,
Where talk is meant and lit, at the throat's hutch,
On streets of blood, in cafés of the lung.

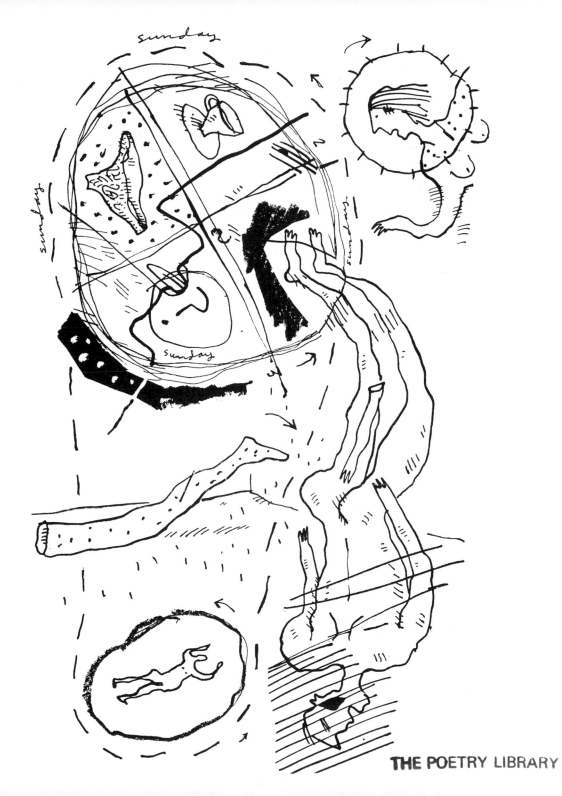

MARGARET MAHY
The Illustrated Traveller's Tale

Possible Nomadic Lines

Wandering through the museum, studying maps of ancient journeys, Helena suddenly felt her skin begin twitching and creeping all over her. Terrified, imagining her surface alive with a network of nomadic yet highly purposeful lines, she fled in under the sign saying: WOMEN, and hid in the nearest lavatory, where she stripped off all her clothes and stood shivering and naked.

Her skin presented its usual surface, not quite smooth but certainly blank. She peered into it, as if she might read a fortune there. Not white, no, though probably more white than any other colour . . . a slightly yellowish white, perhaps, shot with pink, veined with violet, and minutely stippled (now she looked closely) with brown . . . or could it possibly be grey? Unable to make up her mind, she stared at her inner forearm, and held it up in the air to catch a better light from the tiny window high in the wall.

Anyhow, the experience was unsettling. Dressed once more, she plunged out of the museum and set off along unfamiliar paths into the patchy maze of the city, glancing from side to side and listening gratefully to the sharp no-nonsense slap of her shoes on the sunny pavement.

Dramatic Moments in Other Families

IS DI'S HEART BREAKING IN SECRET? asked a poster as Helena walked past a newsagent's. I SAW MY HUSBAND SWIM AWAY WITH A MERMAID, said the one next to it, rustling . . . undulating in the wind. TAIHAPE TRAGEDY – MAN BURSTS INTO FLAMES. NO PREVIOUS COMBUSTION IN FAMILY, SAYS GRIEVING SISTER.

What dramatic lives other families led, thought Helena, and composed a poster for herself: MERIVALE HOUSEWIFE FEELS SKIN COME ALIVE! NOMADIC LINES VANISH ON EXPOSURE TO AIR.

Possible Choices

TATTOOING! said the next shop. LET ME ILLUSTRATE YOU, it suggested in letters of flaking gold. MAPS A SPECIALTY. WITH PAIN OR WITHOUT PAIN. YOUR CHOICE.

'Is there really a choice?' she asked the tattooist who leaned across her doorway, cleaning small fragments of human skin from under her fingernails.

'I dunno,' the tattooist said. 'Could be!'

Her fingers were long and graceful, easily able to stretch a full octave.

In the small window beside the tattooist Helena could see charts showing skulls with scrolls in their teeth, roses, crucifixions, swastikas and dragons. 'But it's so permanent,' she said, 'and apparently you're often sorry afterwards.'

'Whatever you do there's always the risk of being sorry afterwards, right?' said the tattooist. 'Not that I want to start in on the philosophy-kick right now, but there it is. Anyhow, you're fully illustrated already. No space left!'

Helena looked down at her palms. Pink without being rosy.

'I'm all space,' she cried. She smiled and held out her empty hands to prove it.

'Under your sleeves?' asked the tattooist. 'Everywhere that doesn't show? I can just feel those lines seething. That's my skill.'

'I promise you . . . nothing but blank skin! I've just checked up.'

'So? *You* can't see the lines, and if you can't no one else can be expected to . . . no one except a trained perceiver like me, that is. They flash upon that inward eye which is the bliss of solitude. But don't worry about it. It's your choice . . . no big deal.'

This conversation made Helena feel anxious. She smiled and walked quickly away. Once around the corner she rolled up her sleeve and studied her forearm again, felt the lines vanish half a second before her eyes actually fell on them, saw nothing but hairs, a few freckles and scattered pale patches like freckles in reverse, then, finally, the deltas between the veins at her wrist.

Wanting to be home quickly, she hailed a taxi.

Smearing the Why

'Get home safely and spring-clean the wardrobe,' said a voice in her head. Yes! Now, before she was distracted any further, now was the time to spring-clean the wardrobe, a job she had been putting off for seven years. Spring-cleaning the wardrobe would re-establish her. Once anchored by the wardrobe she could ride out any storm. 'My choice!' Helena muttered to herself as the taxi carried her back past the shops. ROYAL COMBUSTION! DI BURSTS INTO FIRE, said one of the posters. The tattooist leaned like a line drawn from side to side of her shop doorway, crossing out the space beyond. She smiled dreamily as she filed her nails.

All the way home, a journey she knew by heart, Helena concentrated on the wardrobe. *Wardrobe*, she thought as she came in through her own door. *Wardrobe*, she thought as she had a quick cup of tea. *Why?* she began to ask herself. *Wardrobe*, she thought quickly, and smashed the wardrobe down hard on the *Why?*, smearing it into a mere stain at the edge of her thoughts.

Spring-cleaning the Wardrobe

The wardrobe was tightly packed. There were the clothes she wore every day, easy to get at, familiar and reassuring. But at either end of the wardrobe, where it was darkest and hardest to reach, hung a queue of half-forgotten shapes all waiting for something . . . waiting until she shrank back to size 12 . . . waiting, with dust on their shoulders, to become fashionable once more. Below the wavering line of hems her shoes stood not quite to attention . . . her sandals, her second-best pair of flat walking shoes, her evening shoes, her joggers. Below these stretched a more pathetic stratum . . . shoes with worn heels or with scuffed toes, not quite good enough to wear or to give to the poor, yet too good to throw away.

Helena flipped through the wardrobe like someone leafing through pages of an autobiography. At the far end where it was dark – there, beyond two long dresses sheathed in plastic – insubstantial fingers advanced slowly to take her hand. They matched her own fingers exactly. Something other than old caftans had been waiting for her. Out it came . . . billowing, shrinking back, then pressing forward once more . . . a graceful silken tissue . . . an old skin that she had shed years ago and must have saved for some reason. Catching on a coat hanger it tore a little, smiling faintly as it did so, then bowed past a winter suit to reintroduce itself to Helena and to recall their old intimate acquaintance.

She stepped back as it drifted out into the room. One of its newly freed hands floated up to its cheek, just as Helena's hand crept to *her* cheek, apparently affected by a residual resonance. As she watched, it grew just a little less transparent. The tear in its shoulder began to mend immediately: the long split which had once begun between the shoulders and run down between the buttocks had well and truly sealed itself during the years of exile at the end of the wardrobe.

The Skin

Why had she saved it? She couldn't begin to remember. When had she come out of this particular skin, anyway? It was slimmer than she was now *and* younger, not new, of course, but suddenly renewed. She imagined herself shedding it, embraced by Brian, perhaps, making love and changing the universe, crying out as it split, sighing with pleasure as she struggled out of it. She imagined how she must have tidied the bed afterwards. She would have put the bottom sheet out for the wash but must have felt a sentimental sympathy for the shed skin . . . a self used up and discarded. Perhaps it had smiled up at her as it smiled now, a confiding ghost, and instead of screwing it up and stuffing it into the approved council rubbish bag she must have tenderly shaken it out and hung it well back in the cupboard among lesser skins, all of which recorded in approximate ways the slope of her shoulders, the curve into her waist, and the unique way her particular feet met the surface of the turning world.

'You silly spook!' she said, amused, admiring the skin's unexpected resilience, for here it was again, pirouetting slowly in a summer draught. It grew even more substantial at the sound of her voice, and turned its head, its smile deepening. She couldn't just push it back among the old clothes, or put it out for the Red Cross. And perhaps she hadn't finished with it, after all? It certainly had not finished with her, for it had taken her hand, and danced around her, reminding her of past possible choices, and even suggesting new ones, perhaps. And why, after all, when her present skin had so recently disconcerted her, had she suddenly decided to tidy the wardrobe?

The phone rang . . . Sally asking about a garden club meeting.

'Sally,' she said. 'What do you do when you shed a skin?'

'Throw it out,' said Sally, puzzled.

'You don't ever keep them?'

'God, no,' Sally said. 'What for?'

'Well, it's like part of you, isn't it?'

'So are nail clippings, but I don't keep them. Do you keep them?'

'Of course not,'

'Well, then . . .'

'I was just wondering . . . suppose you had a skin illustrated . . . tattooed with planets . . . owls . . . bears . . . man-eating plants. I mean, then in a way you'd be illustrated yourself, you'd be like a work of art, but you'd still be free to choose. You wouldn't have to worry about being sorry afterwards.'

'Too gruesome for me,' said Sally. 'And what would Brian say?'

Painting in the Smile

The skin leaned towards the mirror. Its fingers drifted up towards its mist of hair.

Helena put down the receiver with a click. The skin turned at the sound and faced her. On an impulse Helena picked up a lipstick and coloured in its smiling mouth with the dark purplish crimson she used when she wore her Sydney coat, that coat with the floating panels. ('Aubergine!' the woman in the shop had said. 'It's the navy-blue of the nineties.') The effect was startling . . . the semi-translucent naked skin . . . and then the suddenly wide dusky smile, implying a joke it didn't need to tell. The smile floated like a Cheshire Cat's smile, almost unsupported in the summer air.

What filled the skin out . . . made it suddenly three-dimensional? Some sort of osmosis had given substance to the space inside it. Helena even imagined intelligence in the transparent eyes, or, if not intelligence, consciousness, perhaps, something direct and uncomplicated . . . a sort of phototropism. Once she herself had occupied the space now outlined by the skin: her imprint was still within it.

When she walked out into the kitchen it followed her. It floated no longer, but mimicked her free walk, swinging its arms a little, though more slowly, more dreamily, than she swung hers. She began to get dinner ready, and the skin moved around the kitchen. It touched the Portuguese cups though it did not have substance enough to lift them from their hooks. In late-afternoon sunlight it was barely visible. Only the Cheshire Cat smile could be seen as it drifted through the air on a level with her own. This reminded her once more of her brief impulse earlier in the day, the impulse to answer the urgent itching demand of her current skin by having some sign tattooed on her thigh or her upper arm . . . on some place where she could see the picture without having it on public display, a secret instruction laid down for those furthest outposts of self with which she had such tentative connections. She believed that the creeping of her skin had been a nudge, a hint that it wanted to be made eloquent.

The Possibility of Being Sorry Afterwards

But suppose she were to be . . . involved in a car accident, say? Helena saw herself whisked to the hospital in a screaming ambulance, hurried through echoing Gothic corridors all painted white and smelling of disinfectant . . . hurry, hurry . . . into the operating theatre. A nurse masked like a terrorist would cut her bloodstained clothes away and there . . . there . . . look! Oh God! Look! A woman with roses growing out of every aperture. A woman whose bones were pictured on the outside of her skin. A woman with HOT on one breast and COLD on the other. The nurse would spring back, eyes round with distaste over the white sterile mask.

'Doctor, this woman is . . . is . . .'

'Yes, nurse?'

'Tattooed!'

'Get her out of here. Send her to an art gallery.'

What Brian Said

Brian came in.

'Christ!' he said. He was amused but dubious too. 'Last week we had your mother to stay . . . and now this!'

'My mother wasn't much trouble,' she said. 'She likes you better than she likes me. She automatically prefers men to women.'

Brian accepted this, as he would accept any acknowledged scientific fact.

'It just shows . . . you never outgrow an interest in sex,' he said. The skin turned to face him as he moved around it.

'It's not that,' Helena replied. 'My mother grew up thinking that men know the truth, and she thinks that if she hangs around them she might get to know some of it too.'

'Yeah, yeah . . . but where did this spring from?' Brian said.

'The back of the wardrobe,' Helena answered. 'And what it proves is that you can't hold doom at bay by spring-cleaning. I'm never going to spring-clean again.' He laughed, thinking she was joking; but Helena meant it, for other skins might come drifting out at her, and more than one would be too much. Brian looked both revolted and fascinated. He went up to the skin and peered into its lucent face.

'Those were the days!' he said. He smiled. He sighed. The skin's fingers floated out and up to touch his cheek. He shivered, then pushed it away, so that it spun the whole length of the kitchen.

Back at the Tattooist's

Next day the tattooist looked at the skin and frowned.

'It'll be like trying to tattoo water,' she complained.

'Yes, but it seems quite substantial,' Helena said earnestly. The skulls and naked women and roses and eagles on the walls around her sneered at her elegant accent, her lambswool sweater and designer jeans. 'If it tears, it seals again almost at once.'

The skin opened its arms. It tempted the tattooist with pale expanses on which maps and allegories could be inscribed.

'Well, I'll have a go,' the tattooist said grudgingly, but then her face lightened a little. 'It's quite a challenge really.'

The skin nodded agreement.

'No four-letter words,' said Helena. 'No skulls.'

'I once did a very nice line of butterflies for a lady,' the tattooist said. 'Down there, say, two inches under the navel, hovering over the jungle, you might say, from one side right over to the other. Fancy butterflies? I can do you monarchs . . . red admirals . . . mind you, cabbage whites are cheapest.'

'No, it seems a bit too cute,' said Helena. 'I don't know what I want really.'

'Well, how about a crucifixion and a view of Jerusalem right down the back?' said the tattooist. 'Not an up-to-date view, mind you. I work from photographs. Or something classic? A fox hunt?'

'No! I belong to the SPCA,' Helena said. 'No pain! My choice!' She made up her mind. 'I want something with forests,' she said. 'Forests and a sea and islands. You said you had an instinct. Well, use it!'

The tattooist's expression grew wary.

'You'll have to pay, even if it's a cock-up,' she said. 'Or even if you don't like what I come up with. There's my time, and then there's the professional skill and judgement. You don't get that overnight.'

'I realise that,' Helena said. 'Forests. Tulgy woods! Jabberwocks! That sort of thing!'

The tattooist looked at her severely. *Who's being cute now?* But all she said was, 'I don't do them whiffling. No bloody whiffling! OK?'

Helena shrugged apologetically, and after a moment the tattooist nodded.

'It's a challenge,' she said. 'I'll get stuck in over the weekend. I'll probably enjoy it.'

'You're an artist,' said Helena sympathetically. The tattooist reared back.

'Better than that, I'm a tradeswoman,' she answered sternly.

Helena grinned. She lifted her hand to wave goodbye to the skin. After a moment its own hand rose uncertainly. Helena wiggled her fingers in farewell. The skin's fingers played a brief silent scale on the air. She smiled. The painted lips of her skin smiled too, in apparent anticipation, crimson lip folded to lip – a smile like an exotic bud, trembling into flower, thought Helena, or perhaps a tender inner organ made suddenly visible.

Standing Back with Narrowed Eyes

Three days later, the weekend safely negotiated, Helena stood again in the tattooist's shop, face to face with her old skin. She frowned over the new network of lines that had suddenly appeared all over it. They were not quite what she had expected. There were no coherent images. Instead, the skin was covered in an apparently random mixture of blue scrawls and tight spirals that began and ended nowhere. Helena touched them delicately and found them not so much cut into the skin as raised above it. There, under the scribble and at the heart of the spirals, she made out a dotted line of scarlet, not so much a running stitch as a racing one, which set off purposefully at an angle to all other inscriptions. Occasionally this line rose up through the labyrinths of blue, in order to cobble pattern to pattern or even pattern to chaos. Then it dived away, down into the blue once more.

The tattooist watched her frowning over the maze, as she tried to make out just where the rose-red line might lead her.

'Weird, eh?' the tattooist said, and ran her own finger lightly around one spiral. 'The question is, is it where you've been or where you're going? Or it might be a closed system, in which case it's both.'

'Where's the forest?' Helena asked.

'Stand back a bit and narrow your eyes,' the tattooist instructed her. Helena stood back, narrowed her eyes, peered . . . the blue scrabbling lines and spirals resolved into the form of a forest. The skin flexed itself. The cryptic branches shifted as if a wind was passing through them. There . . . there . . . no, *there*, went the red line. A journey through the forest then? Shapes heaved and subsided around the hypothetical traveller who moved on quickly and methodically, having faith in the nature of the journey ahead and refusing to be diverted. Helena envied its purpose and containment. She narrowed her eyes still further . . . found they were closed but that the branches and beasts continued to sway and swell, that the solitary traveller tripped busily on, even behind her eyelids.

'I just laid down what was there already!' the tattooist said. 'That's what you really wanted, wasn't it? To have it marked in so that you could see it too, right?'

'On a separate skin!' Helena said. 'No pain.'

'Your choice!' said the tattooist. 'I dunno, though! I reckon you have to feel pain some of the time, or you'd never know you're travelling, right? And you have to travel in your own skin, I'm sure of that.'

'No one in their right mind would choose pain,' Helena said.

'I reckon you can choose not to notice it,' the tattooist answered. 'And then try to keep on top of it. That's, like, my current theory.'

'You should alter your sign then,' Helena said. 'It's false advertising out there.'

'I'm a tradeswoman,' said the tattooist. 'Not many customers if I told the whole truth! Same problem that God's got, right? God and me, we both have to do a bit of juggling to stay in business, what with the recession and so on.'

The skin had become opaque. The smile, having a more substantial context, no longer floated in the air. The eyes looked darkly back at her, out through the dense blue leaves that had been engraved across its face.

The tattooist saw Helena avoiding the skin's gaze.

'We gave her eyes to see with and lips that she might tell. So she's *her* now, not *it*, and *it* was freer than *her*. Right? Anyhow, take her home now. Live with her for a bit and see how things turn out. I really want to know.'

In the kitchen at home the skin touched the cups again. Now she could actually take them down and hang them up again.

'Leave them!' Helena told her, but the skin gave her what seemed to be an insolent look and insisted on taking the cups down, only to hang them up again in a different order. Watching her in alarm, Helena narrowed her eyes. At once the skin's surface writhed, mouths opened under the net of blue lines, serpents embraced her wrist and forearms and her long legs burst into leaf.

'I'm sorry,' Helena stammered, seeing the burden she had placed upon the skin. 'I know it's really *my* journey . . .'

The smiling lips moved.

'Mine now!' they said . . . Helena supposed they said.

What Brian Said the Second Time Round

'Good heavens,' said Brian, coming into the room behind her. 'What have you done to it? You've ruined it.'

He was staring at the skin with a dismay which rapidly became something more ambivalent.

'There was nothing much there to ruin,' she said. 'It's just a cast-off skin.'

'But I rather liked her the way she was,' he said. 'You've ruined her innocence . . . made her all . . .'

'All . . .?'

'So sinister,' he said with longing. 'You've made her so sinister.'

Later that night Helena woke up in darkness. She heard the clock strike twelve, put out her hand and found she was alone. It came as no surprise to her by then.

Down the Stairs at Midnight

Naked but without anticipation, Helena walked down the stairs at midnight.

There in the last of the firelight Brian was embracing the skin, as if he might, by climbing into it himself, restore its lost innocence. As his hands moved over the skin, the scrolls and spirals, forests, leaves and birds trembled and lived brief lives, fading all the time. For all that, the skin was not real, merely as real as she needed to be.

'And what about me?' Helena wondered. 'Do I go now and hang myself up in the wardrobe waiting to come back into fashion?'

Then she looked intently into her palm and saw, in fine print along the curve of her lifeline, battered golden words: WITH PAIN OR WITHOUT PAIN. YOUR CHOICE. Could there be any real choice when your fortune was already set down in the lines of your palm?

'Well, I'm certainly not going to choose pain,' Helena said. 'To hell with that! I'll set out instead.' She could see the scrolls, scribbles, lines and leaves plainly, but they were where they belonged now, cut into her own flesh in a more intricate pattern than in that first design she had asked the skin to bear for her. The journey was to be even deeper and stranger than it appeared. When she looked up again she saw all lines had faded from the skin that Brian embraced so insistently, leaving it coloured in, yellowish-white, shot with pink, but as blank as she had once believed herself to be.

Setting Out

Helena laughed with surprise. She didn't have to dress for she was already wrapped around in her journey. So she gave the lovers her blessing before setting out into that forest which everyone else believed to be the city. When she wanted to know which path to take she glanced down at her own body, and followed the path taken by the stitching scarlet line, the confident cursor, leaping ahead of her, dancing from word to word of her story.

Later, the tattooist, leaning across the doorway of her shop, watched Helena go by on the other side of the road, and waved a finger at her in acknowledgement, possibly admonishment, and perhaps amusement too. The gesture was certainly a greeting, and at least half a blessing.

PRICELESS ARTWORKS SET OUT ON JUNGLE JOURNEY, said the poster at the newsagent's. CHARLES AND DI DANCE BACK TO BACK. THIRD TEST VICTORY FOR LOCAL SPORTSMEN. END OF THE WORLD PASSES UNNOTICED.

Holding her illustrated arms wide like a loving somnambulist, Helena advanced to envelop the jungle which advanced to greet and envelop her. Just which of them was the embraced and which the embracer was impossible to determine.

DINAH HAWKEN
from A Whole Lot of Small Stories

She and Jung

She and Jung are in a huge bed together caressing each other's right
forearms. He is in his eighties; she in her thirties. I won't make love to
you, he says, unless I can be sure of your respect and commitment.

*　　*　　*

The Tug of War

Is a scene that rises in her mind. A long line of men, say 100
facing north, holding a long rope. A long line of women, say 110
facing south, facing the men, holding the same long rope.
They are all dressed in late-nineteenth-century clothes, standing ready
on the shoreline of a long New Zealand beach. A long line
of surf is breaking.
  The rope is clearly visible in the gap
where the first man faces the first woman. Here the starter also
stands. He is shouting into a megaphone:
'Take the strain – get ready – go!' So the tug
of war begins. Equal weight and equal strength on each
side. Centuries of struggle are rising
in the blood of each man and each woman and at the exact
moment that they judge the men to be at the height
of their physical and mental power, the women
let the rope go.

*　　*　　*

They love to let go and they love to get going:
they get themselves going and they let themselves go.
They let love go and they get love going:
they get others going and they let others go.
They let life go and they get life going,
they live to give love and they love to let live.

Her Cousin Strikes Gold

To her amazement, she discovers that her gruff, conservative, farming cousin is staying with her maverick, lesbian, psychotherapist friend. She meets them together at a party and is very surprised. How on earth did you two meet? she asks. We met on holiday up north, actually we met on a flying fox in an amusement park. She was with Annie and we rode this big metal disc together from the top of a cliff down over this big open beach. It was great. We were the only ones who wanted to do it more than once which is how we met. I think she's great, he says. I admire her. I love her. I'm staying with her because what she says and does is so damned valuable and wise.

*　　*　　*

Here they are now like a wave in the wide bed:
a woman curving round the spine of a woman
who is curving round the spine of a man
who is curving round the spine of a man
who is curving round the spine of a woman
who is curving round the spine of a child.

SALMAN RUSHDIE

Christopher Columbus and Queen Isabella of Spain Consummate their Relationship, Santa Fe, January 1492

Columbus, a foreigner, follows Queen Isabella for an eternity without entirely giving up hope.

– In what characteristic postures?

Proud yet supplicant, the head held high but the knee bent. Fawning yet fearless; possessed of a certain saucy vulgarity, he gets away with it by virtue of his confidence man's charm. However, as time passes, the ingratiating aspects of his stance are emphasised; the sea-dog raffishness wears a little thin. As do his shoes.

– His hope. It is of what?

Obvious answers first: he hopes for preferment. He wants to tie the Queen's favour to his helmet, like a knight in a romance. (He owns no helmet.) He has hopes of cash, and of three tall ships, Niña Pinta Santamaria; of, in fourteen hundred and ninety-two, sailing across the ocean blue. But on his first arrival at court, when the Queen herself asked him what he desired, he bowed over her olive hand and, with his lips a millimetre away from the great ring of her power, murmured a single, dangerous word:

'Consummation.'

– These unspeakable foreigners! The nerve! Consummation, indeed. And then following in her footsteps, month after month, as if he stood a chance. His coarse epistles, his tuneless serenades beneath her casement windows, obliging her to have them closed, shutting out the cooling breeze. She had better things to do, a world to conquer and so forth, who did he think he was? – Foreigners can be dogged. And also, on account of language difficulties, fail to take a hint. Then again, let us not forget, it is considered de rigueur *to keep a few foreigners around. They lend the place a certain cosmopolitan tone. They are often poor and consequently willing to perform divers necessary but dirty jobs. They are, moreover, a warning against complacency, their existence in our midst reminding us that there are quarters in which (hard as it is to accept) we ourselves would be considered foreigners, too. – But to speak so to the Queen! – Foreigners forget their place (having left it behind). Given time, they begin to think of themselves as our equals. It is an unavoidable hazard. They*

introduce into our austerities their Italianate blandishments. Nothing for it. Turn a deaf ear, look the other way. They rarely mean real harm, and go too far only infrequently. The Queen, be assured, can look after herself.

Columbus at Isabella's court is quickly burdened with the reputation of a crazy man. His clothes are excessively colourful and he drinks, also, to excess. When Isabella wins a military victory she celebrates it with eleven days of psalms and the sonorous severities of priests. Columbus crashes about outside the cathedral waving a wineskin. He is a one-man debauch.

– See him, the drunkard, his huge shaggy head filled with nonsenses! A fool with a glittering eye dreaming of a golden paradise beyond the western edge of things.

'Consummation.'

The Queen plays with Columbus.

She promises him everything he wants at luncheon and cuts him dead later the same afternoon, looking through him as if he were a veil.

On his saint's day she summons him into her inmost boudoir, dismisses her girls, permits him to braid her hair and for a moment to fondle her breasts. Then she summons her guards. For forty days she banishes him to the stables and piggeries. He sits forlorn on horse-munched hay while his thoughts run on distant, fabled gold. He dreams of the Queen's perfumes but awakes, gagging, in a pigsty.

Toying with Columbus pleases the Queen.

And pleasing the Queen, he reminds himself, may help him to achieve his purposes. Pigs rootle by his feet. He grits his teeth. 'Pleasing the Queen is good.'

– Does she torment him merely for sport?

Or: because he is foreign and she is unused to his ways and meanings.

Or: because her ring finger, still hot with the memory of his lips, his breath, has been – how-you-say? – *touched*. Tentacles of warmth spread backwards from her finger towards her heart. A turbulence has been aroused.

Or: because she is torn between the possibility of embracing his scheme with a lover's abandon, and the more conventional, and differently (maliciously) pleasurable option of destroying him by laughing, finally, after much foreplay, in his foolish supplicant face.

Columbus consoles himself with possibilities. Not all possibilities are consoling, however.

She is an absolute monarch. (Her husband is an absolute zero: a blank, couldn't be colder. We will not speak further of him.) She is a woman whose ring is often kissed. It means nothing to her. She is no stranger to blandishments. She resists them effortlessly. She is a tyrant who numbers among her possessions a private menagerie of four hundred and nineteen fools, some grotesquely malformed, others as beauteous as the dawn. He, Columbus, is merely her four hundred and twentieth idiot. He is her clown, her performing flea. This, too, is a plausible scenario.

Either: she understands him, his dream of a world beyond the world's end, so profoundly that she's spooked by it, she turns first towards it, then away;

or: she doesn't understand him at all, nor cares to understand.

Take your pick.

What's certain is that *he* doesn't understand *her*. Only the facts are plain. She is Isabella, all-conquering Queen. He is her invisible (though raucous, multicoloured, wine-bibbing) man.

'Consummation.'

The sexual appetites of the male decline; those of the female continue, with the advancing years, to grow. Isabella is Columbus's last hope. He is running out of possible patrons, sales talk, flirtatiousness, hair, steam. Time drags by. Isabella gallops around, winning battles, expelling Moors from strongholds, her appetites expanding by the week. The more of the land she swallows, the more warriors she engulfs, the hungrier she gets. Columbus, aware of a slow shrivelling inside him, scolds himself. He should see things as they are. He should come to his senses. What chance does he have here? Some days she makes him clean latrines. On other days he is on body-washing duty and after a battle the bodies are not clean. Soldiers going to war wear man-sized nappies under their armour because the fear of death will open the bowels, will do it every time. Columbus was not cut out for this sort of work. It is getting him nowhere. He tells himself to leave Isabella, once and for all.

But there are problems: his advancing years, the patron shortage. Once he decamps, he will have to forget the western voyage. The body of philosophical opinion which avers that life is absurd has never appealed to him. He is a man of action, revealing himself by deeds. But without the possibility of the voyage he will be obliged to accept the meaninglessness of life. This, too, would be a defeat. Invisible in hot tropical colours, unrequited, he remains, dogging her footsteps, hoping for the ecstasy of her glance.

'The search for money and patronage,' Columbus says, 'is not so different from the quest for love.'

*　　*　　*

– She is omnipotent. Castles fall at her feet. The Jews have been expelled. The Moors prepare their last surrender. The Queen is at Granada, riding at her armies' head. – She overwhelms. Nothing she has wanted has ever been refused. All her dreams are prophecies. Acting upon information received while sleeping, she draws up her invincible battle plans, foils the conspiracies of assassins, learns of the infidelities and corruptions for which she blackmails both her loyalists (to ensure their support) and her opponents (to ensure theirs). The dreams help her forecast the weather, negotiate treaties, and invest shrewdly in trade. – She eats like a horse and never gains an ounce. The earth adores her footfall. Its shadows flee before the brilliance of her eyes. Her face is a lush peninsula set in a sea of hair. Her treasure chests are inexhaustible. Her ears are soft question marks, suggesting some uncertainty. Her legs. – Her legs are not so great.

　　– She is full of discontents.

　　– No conquest satisfies her, no peak of ecstasy is high enough.

　　See: there at the gates of the Alhambra is Boabdil the Unlucky, the last Sultan of the last redoubt of all the centuries of Arab Spain. Behold: now, at this very instant, he surrenders the keys to the citadel into her grasp: there! – And as the weight of the keys falls from his hand into hers, she, she, yawns.

Columbus gives up hope.

While Isabella is entering the Alhambra in listless triumph, he is saddling his mule. While she dawdles in the Courtyard of the Lions, he departs in a frenzy of whips, elbows, hooves, all rapidly obscured by a dust-cloud. Invisibility claims him. He surrenders to its will. Knowing he is abandoning his destiny, he abandons it. He rides away from Queen Isabella in hopeless fury, rides day and night, and when his mule dies under him he shoulders his ridiculous gipsy patchwork bags, their rowdy colours muted now by dirt; and walks. Around him stretches the lush plain her armies have subdued. Columbus sees none of it, not the land's fertility nor the sudden barrenness of the vanquished castles looking down from their pinnacles. The ghosts of defeated civilisations flow unnoticed down the rivers, Guadalthis and Guadalthat, their names retaining an echo of the annihilated past. Overhead, the arabesque wheelings of the patient buzzards. Jews pass Columbus in long columns, but the tragedy of their expulsion makes no mark on him. Somebody tries to sell him a Toledo sword; he waves the man away. Having lost his own dream of ships, Columbus leaves the Jews to the ships of their exile, waiting in the harbour of Cadiz. Exhaustion strips him of his senses. This old world is too old and the new world is an unfound land.

'The loss of money and patronage,' Columbus says, 'is as bitter as unrequited love.'

He walks beyond fatigue, beyond the limits of endurance and the frontiers of self, and somewhere along this path he loses his balance, falls off the edge of his sanity, and out here beyond his mind's rim he sees, for the first and only time in his life, a vision.

It's the dream of a dream. He dreams of Isabella, languidly exploring the Alhambra, the great jewel she has seized from Boabdil, last of the Nasrids. She is staring into a large stone bowl held aloft by stony lions. The bowl is filled with blood, and in it she sees (Columbus dreams her seeing) a vision of her own.

The bowl shows her that everything, all the known world, is now hers; everyone in it is in her hands, to do with as she pleases. And when she understands this (Columbus dreams) the blood at once congeals, becoming a thick and verminous sludge. Whereupon the Isabella of Columbus's weary, but also vengeful imaginings is shaken to her very marrow by the realisation that she will never, *never*, NEVER! be satisfied by the possession of the known. Only the unknown, perhaps even the unknowable, can satisfy her. And at once she remembers Columbus, he envisions her remembering him, the invisible man who dreams of entering the invisible world, the unknown and perhaps even unknowable world beyond the edge of things, beyond the stone bowl of the everyday, beyond the thick blood of the sea. Columbus in this bitter dream makes Isabella see the truth at last, makes her accept that her need for him is as great as his for her. Yes! She knows it now! She must must must give him the money, the ships, anything, and he must must must carry her flag and her favour beyond the end of the end of the earth, into exaltation and immortality, linking them for ever with bonds far harder to dissolve than those of any mortal love, the harsh and deifying ties of history.

'Consummation.'

Isabella, in Columbus's savage dream, tears her hair, runs from the Court-yard of the Lions, screams for her heralds. 'Find him,' she commands. But Columbus in his dream refuses to be found. He wraps around himself the dusty patchwork cloak of his invisibility and the heralds gallop hither and yon in vain. Isabella screeches, beseeches, implores. Bitch, bitch. How do you like it now, Columbus sneers. By absenting himself from her court, by this final and suicidal invisibility, he has denied her her heart's desire. Serves her right. Bitch! She murdered his hopes, didn't she? Well then. In doing so she has laid herself low as well. Poetic justice. Fair's fair.

At the dream's end he permits her messengers to find him. Their hoofbeats, their waving frantic arms. They plead, cajole, offer bribes. But it's too late. Only the sweet self-lacerating joy of murdering possibility remains. He answers the heralds: a shake of the head. *No.*

He comes to his senses. He is on his knees in the fertility of the plains, waiting for death. He hears the hoofbeats approaching, and raises his eyes, half-expecting to see the exterminating angel, riding towards him like a conqueror. Its black wings, the boredom on its face.

Isabella's heralds surround him. They offer him food, drink, a horse.

Good news, they shout. The Queen has summoned you. Your voyage: wonderful news. She saw a vision, and it scared her.

All her dreams are prophecies.

She ran from the Courtyard of the Lions, shouting for you, the heralds report. She will send you beyond the stone bowl of the known world, beyond the thick blood of the sea. She's waiting for you in Santa Fe. You must come at once.

He stands up, like a requited lover, like a groom on his wedding day. He opens his mouth and it almost spills out, the bitter refusal: no.

'Yes,' he tells the heralds. *Yes. I'll come.*

ROBERT CRAWFORD

Two Poems

Prayer

Upstream from shattered urban lintels
Lost crofts are soft as new bread.

That dripping tap in the one-walled kitchen
Reminds someone there will be a need
Of water before and after.

Sin to imagine a perfect world
Without embarrassment, rain, or prayer.
A hand is clasping my other hand

In a dark place that has to be got through
On a wing and. Listen to this.

X

I see your face in the light's east neuk
At Pittenweem or St Andrews.

Between stalks of rye I glimpse an oil rig
Being towed away into the light.

What are you saying? I can see just lips'
Fricatives and plosives. To make you out

I have to move from the west to the east,
To where wind rattles corrugated iron

On a silage shed, then along low hilltops
At the entrance to the Kingdom of Fife.

A fighter skims Leuchars station's rooftiles. Swifts
Do the same at the Falkland Palace

You ignored in childhood to print on a beach
The word you begin with, Alice.

Euro-

Man

NEW

O L D

JANE CAMPION
Big Shell

During the Christmas break I worked at a souvenir shop that sold shells. In this shop was the biggest shell I had ever seen. It would have come up to my knee and it wasn't for sale. The owner had fitted a light inside it and it sat in the front window and glowed. The colours were all colours of pink: purple-pink, cream-pink, and where the shape curled inside itself the pinks became very dark, almost black.

I got this job because I didn't have any money and I didn't have any confidence to go and sell myself as an art director, especially before Christmas when everything was jolly.

A month or so ago I'd finally finished with my boyfriend. I only got the strength to do that because of this course I did. At the time, I realised all these things about myself and him, and I was very clear that the relationship was not 'an opening for possibility'. I realised that he had 'a negative conversation' about me and my relationship with him was 'based on complaint'.

John was gone and he took his mirror. It was a door off a wardrobe that used to lean up against the wall in my room, so I could always check myself before I came in or went out. That's what got me; looking to see myself and my not being there. That's when I realised he'd gone. I went right down in a big spiral. Once I felt I was going down, I stopped trying to be bright or happy, I decided to go right on down, as down as down could go.

My buddy from the course rang me up one evening.

'Hello, this is Fran Basset, your buddy.'

'Oh, you must be looking for Lou – she's not here,' I lied.

'Oh right. Well, could you tell Lou I just rang to find out how she was going with her commitments.'

In a journal I wrote: 'John, oh God, I miss you.' Then I divided the page into two separate columns and wrote at the top of one column: 'Positive aspects of being alone,' and on the other: 'Negative aspects of being alone.' Under 'Positive' I wrote: 'No arguments about housework.' Then I rang up a friend.

'Hello, Kay.'

'Oh Lou, how are you? Still high from that thing you did?'

'Not really, I'm a bit depressed.'

'Oh, why?'

'Oh, you know, everything, no John, being alone. No work right now . . .'

'You've got to pull yourself out of this . . .'

'Hmm . . .'

'It's self-indulgent . . . hold on . . .'

I listened to the sound of her baby screaming. It seemed very distant as if it was coming from across a big green glade.

Pull yourself together. Shit. I thought: I'm always doing that. No, I'm not going to this time. I'm going to fall apart.

Anyhow, I ran out of money and got this job selling shells, mostly to tourists. An American came in with slacks and runners, he looked right at me and said, 'So she-sells-seashells. You know what I want? I want that damn giant.'

'Well, I can't sell you that seashell, it's not for sale.'

'It's good, though. Huh, I bet it gets them in here.'

'I don't know really. I haven't been here so long.'

That afternoon a guy in a wheelchair came into the shop; he was pretty young and I guessed from the States. I like people in chairs because they remind me of my brother, though this guy was nothing like Trevor, he was a Yankee tourist with a nylon money-belt and a whole pile of badges stuck to his chair.

He said, 'Hi there, how ya doin'?'

After he'd looked at both sides of the shop he said, 'That's some shell you got in yer window. Hey, you been to Bris-bane?'

I said that I had once.

'Yeah, I'm doin' some tour of the Gold Coast. I've been to Perth and Cairns. It's more economic to do Bris-bane from Sydney, so I'm doin' it that-a-way.'

'Great,' I said, 'have fun.'

'Yeah, I hope so.'

As he wheeled out I followed him and gave him my phone number. I offered to show him something of Sydney.

He said, 'That's fine, 'cause I got four days in Sydney before I fly to Papua New Guinea. They got big shells there too,' he added.

'I didn't know.'

'Yeah, I read it. They swap them for wives and things. Have a good day.'

My brother Trevor was disabled from birth. He didn't like other disabled people, he called them cripples, frothers and half-wits. My brother played lead guitar in his school rock group. Beautiful, intelligent girls took turns to wheel him to school.

He's dead now. He got into drugs when he left home. First his girlfriend Vivian over-dosed, then after that, when he came home to live, Mum found him with a blue plastic bag over his head, tied around his neck. Mum thought he was joking at first. But Trevor was dead.

Trevor told me he was a great fuck, because he was very still. He said stillness is what the 'rooters' never learn. He said sensitive girls appreciated the aesthetics of still sex, it made them feel powerful and it was much more subtle and erotic.

Vivian and I went shoe-shopping one Saturday. She told me that once Trevor peed on her by mistake, and because she laughed he wouldn't let her near him, not ever again. She was pretty far gone by then, very thin. I'm not sure, but I believe it's possible she got their dope from prostitution.

When I did the course, I stood up and shared about Trevor. I put my hand up and the leader read out my nametag.

'Yes, Louise.'

I stood up and an assistant ran, crouching, towards the edge of my row. He passed the microphone along the row until I could take it.

'I'm very sad because I never told my brother how much I loved him.'

'Is your brother dead?'

'Yes.'

'And you didn't tell him?'

'No.'

'Good, I got it. Are you complete about that?'

'Yes.'

'Thank you, Louise.'

Everybody clapped and I handed the microphone back along the row until the crouching assistant took it and ran crouching back.

'Lou, guess who this is.'

I had no idea, but I could hear lots of noise in the background.

'Sorry, who is it?'

'You gotta guess.'

'I can't. Who is it?'

'Now, come on, try . . .'

I put the phone down and went back to watching my television set which I have to keep my toe on to get a good picture. The phone rang again with the same long-distance peeps.

'Hello, Lou, it's me, Dale, remember? I'm up in Surfer's Paradise.'

'Oh right, why didn't you say?'

'I was just playing about. I guess you weren't in the mood, huh?'

'Not really. How is it?'

'It's OK. No, I'm kiddin', it's wild! I get back tomorrow afternoon, so, Lou, you wanna go sight-see?'

Dale arranged to meet me outside the shell shop. He was late, so I amused myself by looking at our big shell. I tried to imagine the size of the creature that lived inside it. It must have been very, very big. A huge, boneless slug with grey, snail-like skin, that could contract and expand as it moved itself along.

When Dale wheeled up, he was wearing a T-shirt that had a shapely woman's bottom drawn on it and underneath in black letters: WHAT A BUMM-ER GOLD COAST.

'Hi there, how yer doin'?'

I couldn't take my eyes off the T-shirt.

'That T-shirt, Dale, is horrible.'

'Yeah, it's bad taste, huh?'

'Yes, it is.'

'I tell you, there's worse.'

I was starting to feel depressed about being with someone in a T-shirt like that. Dale started to look depressed too.

'It's a joke T-shirt, Lou, a joke.'

It was after our Opera House tour, after Dale had put a jersey over his T-shirt (despite the heat and his sweating) that I realised I was in love with him. I decided he was the most courageous man I had ever met. My love-eyes focused in on his brown eyes, carefully avoiding his hair, which wasn't washed and anyway didn't have any style and slid down to his lips which were very young-looking. He was sipping a *cappuccino*, and while he told me about his South American tour I started to imagine him undressed. I thought about his legs and how I could gently lift them, white and thin, on to the bed. He'd probably have a colostomy bag and I'd slip that lower down in the bed under the sheet. Then I'd touch him slowly all over, possibly the first person ever to do that, and he'd lie there and maybe even cry. Then we'd maybe make the slow still sex that Trevor had talked about. That was, if he could have erections, otherwise maybe we'd just kiss.

I wasn't asleep to the idea that this might be some sex ode to my dead brother. But Dale was not Trevor.

Dale didn't seem to know self-pity. When I told him I'd been depressed because my boyfriend and I had broken up, he looked sad because I looked sad, but mostly puzzled.

I said, 'You've never been depressed?'

'Nope.'

'Are you sure – not ever? What about when you were a teenager?'

'Nope.'

'What about school sports day?'

'Nope, I just stayed home an' watched the box.'

'You can't ever remember being depressed?'

'Nope.'

Dale said he had to go because his hostel had a curfew. I said I'd drive him.

In the car I said, 'Why don't you come home and have a look at my flat?'

'Gee, I'd like that, but I'd miss the curfew.'

'Well, you could stay the night. I've got a sofa-bed.'

He took a while to answer.

'I guess you're a bit lonely.'

'Yes, I am a bit,' I said, irritated, 'but that's not why I'm asking you.'

By the time I got to my place Dale seemed tired.

'Lou, what floor are you on?'

'Oh shit. Oh Dale, I can't believe I didn't think of it.'

The challenge of the steps seemed to cheer Dale up. He gave precise and encouraging instructions to me. He kept on saying, 'I'm not heavy,' and laughing. I thought of Robert de Niro in *The Mission*, dragging all those things up the waterfall, and I started to believe I'd get my salvation out of this. I didn't know why Dale wasn't worried. I honestly, twice, nearly lost him.

He said, 'Oh-oh, close.'

When we both had a glass of wine in our hands and I'd had a shower I decided to tell Dale I loved him.

'Really.' He looked puzzled, then raised his eyebrows and said, 'Gee.'

I said he could sleep on the sofa-bed if he liked but I'd love it if we could sleep together.

'Lou, I'm not sure.'

'Well, do you like me?'

'Yes, I do, but you're quite a bit older than me.'

'Yes, I know that. Nine years.'

'Let me think about it a moment.'

'Are you scared about something?'

'No.'

'OK.'

I moved a bit closer to him and said, 'Well, Dale, I'm going to bed now so I'll put down the sofa. You'll have to move back because it fills this space here, and then you can choose where you'd prefer to sleep.'

Dale wheeled into the toilet, where I guess he was emptying his bag. I heard the toilet flush, so I supposed that's what he was up to. When he came out he wheeled into my bedroom.

'Wow, dim lights, satin cover and everything, Lou.'

By the time I got to the doorway he was looking up at the wall reading one of my affirmations.

'Dale, I feel a lot of love for you, but it's quite OK by me that you don't. What's not OK is that you treat me, my love and my bedroom as a joke. So out you go to the sofa-bed, go on, you and your horrible T-shirt.'

'Hey, Lou, can't I sleep in here?'

'Not like that. No.'

'Well, I'm sorry. You know, Lou, it would be a real adventure to sleep here with you, and what the heck, that's what I'm here for.'

'You're a jerk, Dale. I don't know why I said I love you.'

'Lou, I love you too. It's just not how I was expecting it.'

I calmed down and sat on the bed looking at my toes. He wheeled close and put a hand on my leg. He didn't just leave it there, he kept patting it in a nervous way, until it started to grate and I held it still.

'I don't mean to hurt yer feelings, Lou, but I never thought my first girl would . . . . well . . . . have wrinkles.' Then he started laughing like it was really hilarious.

'Oh, what did you expect?'

'Nothing really. Heck, I'm a regular guy. I just wanted some girl with smooth long hair, brown or blonde, who looks hot in jeans . . . Hey, what are yer doin'?'

I had taken hold of his chair and was wheeling it out to the sofa-bed.

'Lou, don't!' He was mad. Then he put the brakes on and I couldn't shift it at all.

'Well, wheel yourself.'

'Thank you, I will!'

I went back to my bedroom, closed the door and turned out the light. I lay on the bed stiff with anger. I must have fallen asleep because I woke up to

Dale, in his chair, already parked next to the bed. He spoke in a soft, almost little boy's voice.

'Lift me into your bed, Lou.'

He had taken his clothes off and just had on his BUMM-ER T-shirt. His legs were white and very thin. Not so much legs, but more like a tadpole's tail, or the see-through legs tadpoles first develop before they become frogs. They felt dead because they were so cold and lifeless. He was heavy, but I could hold him, and when he put his arms around my neck to help me, I kissed him on the cheek. I laid him down on the bed and I asked him where he wanted to put the bag.

'Oh, just down beside me, thanks.'

I kissed him on the lips this time, and he kissed back so hard I couldn't really feel a thing.

'Softly, Dale.'

He softened up and we kissed for a bit more, then he started crying, big, gulpy, painful tears.

'Dale, let's stop. Just relax and go to sleep.'

I cradled him in my arms and, half-sobbing, he snuggled his head up towards my chest and hungrily, like an animal, he started to suck.

'Ouch, Dale, gently!'

He was in a kind of animal overdrive. I liked it even though it felt strange, like being intimate with a different species.

I looked down at his face, it was all screwed up. I felt a lump deep in my chest, a definite physical presence, that painfully and slowly started to move upwards until I felt this same lump in my throat. The lump rested there a while, before starting my lips off quivering and my eyes blinking and then, as the lump came into my mouth and finally out into the world, my body started shaking and a whole series of little gulps and cries came up out of me. I was panting and blubbing and holding on to Dale, stroking his head, thinking of him as a lame frog who was magically gifted to save me from my unhappiness.

It must have been very late, maybe 3 a.m. Dale was still licking and sucking, making little 'oh-h, oh-h, oh-h' moaning sounds. Then he stopped and got very serious.

'Touch my penis, Lou – you'd know – is that hard enough?'

'Don't worry about it. I'm not even on the pill.'

'Just tell me, though, is that hard enough?'

I did touch it and it wasn't really hard, sort of gumbi-hard.

'It feels nice.'

He made another strange sound and was still.

'What is it?'

'I gotta stop this.'

'What's up?'

'Nothing. I just gotta stop, that's all.'

He pulled his BUMM-ER T-shirt down and fitted the sheet around himself.

In the morning when I woke Dale wasn't there. I lay still and listened. In the next room I could hear Dale moving. I found him on the floor, next to the sofa-bed, with his jeans halfway up his legs. He didn't take any notice of me and continued pushing each dead leg further down the jeans.

'Do you want tea?'

He just kept on.

'Dale, do you want tea?'

'No thanks.'

I went on through to the kitchen to start my breakfast. I couldn't work out what he was about. Watching him from the kitchen he looked odd and deformed. A baby with hairy arms.

'Dale, tell me what I can do to help you.'

His face was so stiff he couldn't talk. I went over to him and knelt beside him.

'What's going on? Why are you so silent?'

Dale didn't look at me.

'Shall I get your chair?'

He nodded. I went into the bedroom to fetch it for Dale but I couldn't work out how to get it out of gear.

'Sorry, Dale, how do you get this thing moving?'

'I'll do it.'

I went back to the kitchen and made myself a peppermint tea. Dale turned himself over and began dragging himself along the floor to my bedroom. His legs rocked to and fro making skid-marks on the carpet. I waited for him to get to my room then followed him in there.

'Can I help you into it?'

'Yeah.'

I supported his weight around my neck and hoisted him up over the chair.

'What's going on with you, Dale?'

He fussed about with his chair, turning levers.

'Silly,' I said, ruffling his hair. He moved his head away from my hand.

'I gotta call a taxi. I'm on a city tour this morning.'

He dialled a number and looked down at the telephone table.

'I don't wanna miss it, this tour goes all over, Bondi, the zoo, Centrepoint Tower.'

'I could've dropped you off, Dale.'

'Thanks, but I'm in a hurry and I don't wanna interfere with you.'

When the taxi came I helped the driver with Dale and the stairs. I took a kitchen chair and put it down on the landing. Then the driver carried Dale down the steps and put him on the chair. We went back up and together we carried Dale's chair to the very bottom. The driver went back up the steps to the landing and carried Dale back down to his own chair. It seemed impossible that I had last night hauled Dale and his chair up the two flights of stairs all alone.

'Have a good tour, and Dale, give me a call.'

'OK.'

From my front door I watched him being lifted into the taxi. I couldn't hear, but I could see him leaning forward and talking and I could see the driver leaning back, nodding and talking animatedly. They were getting on very well.

I rang the shell shop and told them I couldn't come in, then I cleaned up the flat and went back to bed. I slept till the afternoon. When I woke up I telephoned the shell shop. No one had rung. I started to write Dale a letter. By 12 p.m. he hadn't rung and I was still trying to get the letter right. When I went to bed I could see Dale's drag-marks on the carpet. When Trevor was alive, we had those marks all up and down our hall.

In the morning, before work at the shop, I took my letter to his hostel. It was early, 8 a.m., so I just left it at the desk. The girl there said she'd make sure he got it. I wish now I'd gone up and given it to him myself. I can't believe that if he got the letter he wouldn't have contacted me.

The day before I left the shell shop I had a dream about the big shell. I dreamt that Dale was inside it and all I could see of him was his thin legs. I was talking to him but he didn't answer. In my dream I wasn't sure he could hear from inside the shell.

On Sunday I left the shell shop for good. The shell was definitely a giant, but nobody could possibly fit in it. Not even a child or a baby.

SEAMUS HEANEY
Two Poems
Mint

It looked like a clump of small dusty nettles
Growing wild at the gable of the house
Beyond where we dumped our tins and bottles.
Usual and unverdant, a bit like us.

But, to be fair, it also spelled promise
And newfangledness in the yard of our life,
As if something vivid and tenacious
Sauntered in green alleys and grew rife.

The snip of scissor blades, the light of Sunday
Mornings when the mint was cut and loved:
My last things will be first things slipping from me.
Yet let all things go free that have survived.

Let the smells of mint go heady and defenceless
Like inmates liberated in that yard.
Like the disregarded ones we turned against
Because we'd failed them by our disregard.

The Articulation of Siberia

When the deaf phonetician spread his hand
Over the dome of a speaker's skull
He could tell which diphthong and which vowel
By the bone vibrating to the sound.

A globe stops spinning. I feel my palm
On a forehead cold as permafrost
And imagine axle-hum and the steadfast
Russian of Osip Mandelstam.

LLOYD JONES
The Simpsons in Russia

Sometimes they held hands, but not very often. As far as Mr Simpson was concerned, holding hands was ridiculous, and his wife knew well enough how it irritated him. But, when the bus had left the border to enter Russia and Maggie took her husband's hand, there was no attempt to wrestle it away. The Simpsons were on their way to Leningrad, at the thought of which Mr Simpson managed a smile: Leningrad, and the idea of taking a bus there. On two occasions he had taken an intercity bus – once, while work was being done on the car; and another time, after Wellington Airport was fogged in, he had bussed up to Palmerston North. But Leningrad could not be mentioned in the same breath as these other times of inconvenience. Great armies had marched on Leningrad.

It was Maggie who had planned the trip. Two weeks ago Mr Simpson was reading the Sunday papers in Holland Park and Maggie had asked if he would like an ice-cream. She left him sitting on the bench for rather a long time; at least it had seemed that way as the sun faded over the city into a bank of cloud. Picnickers reached for pullovers; Mr Simpson rubbed his bare arms. Frankly, it was irritating to wait that long, particularly so when he viewed his wife returning across the grass empty-handed. She hadn't been able to find an ice-cream vendor, and Mr Simpson had rolled his eyes: it was ridiculous not to be able to find ice-cream in a park on a Sunday afternoon. His wife had walked all the way to Kensington, where she realised – 'Silly me,' she said – that an ice-cream would not survive the return journey. This was the news she returned with, before presenting him with a small cardboard notice. Maggie had found it pinned to a bulletin board in a shop entranceway. The notice – written in both English and possibly Russian – invited 'interested parties' to join a bus tour to Leningrad.

Ice-cream, thought Mr Simpson at the passing scenery in the bus window, and alternatively: So this is Russia. It did not seem like a superpower. There was barely any traffic on the road, and the passing farmland looked unproductive and unkempt. All the same he was glad they were off to Leningrad – and not, say, Rome, or Venice, or those other postcard cities. The Simpsons didn't know anybody who had been to Leningrad; not even Yvonne, their oldest daughter who taught English to businessmen in Turkey.

They had had to get themselves to Berlin. The rendezvous was a street corner in the Kreuzberg where the unexpected number of daytime prostitutes, Turks, kebab bars and nightclubs had caused the Simpsons some alarm. Mrs Simpson had needed to push her husband from behind to get him to board the bus. It was her idea. She had to provide the enthusiasm. Put a brave face on things. Out the bus window, Mr Simpson had watched a young man sit down in a shop doorway, roll up a shirtsleeve and plunge a needle into his arm. Mr Simpson felt a sudden rush of panic; and it was perhaps just as well that the way out was blocked by their fellow passengers humping suitcases and cardboard boxes along the aisle. He could smell food, foreign food – the sharp rotten smell of unrefrigerated meat, and forgotten cheese. This was the other time on the trip Maggie had reached for his hand and given it a firm squeeze, as if to say, Everything will be all right.

Last night they had driven through Poland. Around dawn Mr Simpson briefly woke to discover they were in a city. He thought it might be Warsaw; and he had thought about waking Maggie to say they were in Warsaw, but instead he fell asleep again, and the next time he woke they were travelling in the countryside. It wasn't until the bus had reached the border, or shortly before it, that the Simpsons were given a 'reststop'.

Tonight they would be in Kaunas; Daugavpils; Riga around dawn; late afternoon, Pskov; and Leningrad later that night.

Mr Simpson started a letter to Yvonne. He wrote that they had spent much of the day passing through 'no-account country'. But he fell asleep before he could explain himself.

Shortly before dusk the bus stopped, but not at Kaunas. Mr Simpson had brought a map with him, and he could see they were a short distance east of where the itinerary placed them. Tall pines made a secret of the surrounding countryside. They had stopped at a restaurant and a warm and almost circular glow in the distance suggested they were on the outskirts of a small town.

'Look here,' Mr Simpson said to the Greek driver. 'Shouldn't we be in Kaunas?' The driver gazed at the plastic which covered Mr Simpson's map, then at Mr Simpson with a flicker of contempt for his need to know, as if to say, I decide. Me. The driver! Mr Simpson trailed after him.

He could hear his wife saying, 'I'm sure it is all right. There's no point in our worrying.' Then she said, 'Look, we're the only ones not inside the restaurant.' He turned back to her. Suddenly they could hear voices, and laughter, and even what sounded like tears. Over the windows of the restaurant were wooden shutters and a warm glow at the bottom of each sill. It occurred to Mr Simpson that they were the only ones left outside. Alone, out here in the Russian night, thought Mr Simpson. Well, it was not quite night because they could see the tops of the pines. But Mr Simpson thought it might be a moment worth telling about once they got home. It would be something Maggie would bring up. Bill, why don't you tell Paddy and Dan about that time in Russia . . . His wife would have on oven-gloves and she would be holding an oven-hot casserole dish, and he would shoot a quick look of disapproval, or perhaps laugh, as if she had rekindled a lost memory.

They walked along a path of trodden pine needles. Mr Simpson allowed his hand to be held, but inside the restaurant, in the cloakroom area, he shook free. Through another set of doors a speech was in progress. Mr Simpson braced himself for the moment when a roomful of faces would stare his and Maggie's way; but none did. They pushed through the swing doors and no one paid the Simpsons the slightest attention. A man with greying hair and a sad drooping moustache was giving the speech. At times he interrupted himself to blow his nose and brush away a tear. Mr Simpson's eye moved to the far end of the room, where in an open doorway he saw the driver seated at a table. He had started on his food and ate hungrily from a fork, while keeping his other hand on the stem of a wine glass for fear it would be removed, or stolen. None of what was happening in the restaurant seemed to be of concern to him.

There were two long tables set with white tablecloths. Bouquets of wild flowers were set between carafes of spring water. Now, at last, a man in a waistcoat, an older man about Mr Simpson's age, found them a place at the bottom end of the second table. The Simpsons stepped over a bench and sat down. The Russian bent down and spoke in Mr Simpson's ear, but it was unintelligible. Mr Simpson spoke in English. He said he was sorry. The waiter shushed him. He held up the palms of his hands, as if Mr Simpson had expressed impatience.

The speech had come to an end, and now the speaker began to read from a list of names: 'Serge.' A man got up from the Simpsons' table. A second name was called: 'Marisha.'

Slowly, a woman rose from the other table. The entire room raised its eyes with her. The man 'Serge' held out his hands and the woman walked over to where he stood, and took both his hands. A woman at the other table was crying loud, painful sobs. Then the speaker held up his glass and offered a toast and on either side of the Simpsons glasses were raised. The Simpsons tried to follow suit but were raising their own as the rest of the glasses in the room were returned to their resting places. Applause broke out. From both tables people called out 'Marisha' and 'Serge'. The woman blushed despite her tears. Sunshine in the rain, thought Mr Simpson. Room was made at the top end of the Simpsons' table, and the couple sat down. The woman began touching the man's face with her fingertips. Mr Simpson hurriedly looked away. He studied his napkin.

The name 'Andrei' was called out, and Mr Simpson looked up at the man who had sat across the aisle on the bus. This morning he had offered Maggie a carrot smeared with horse radish. Mr Simpson had declined it with a wave of his hand. Maggie had smiled, and said, 'No thank you very much.' They had their water crackers and tea flask.

Now this same man left the table to run and hug 'Lenka', a woman unused to make-up, perhaps, and whose hair more usually was kept in a scarf. The woman had dressed and made herself up elaborately; a little ambitiously, felt Mr Simpson. The women whose names were called appeared older than the men. Their faces bore the lines of perseverance Mr Simpson had seen in old *National Geographics*: – on the faces of Soviet women in overalls and scarves, shouldering brooms and shovels.

Not everyone stood up and paired off, thankfully. And soon the business was completed, and the Simpsons were fed a watery stew of potatoes and cabbage. The man alongside pointed to the contents of his glass, and said, 'Schnapps.' Mr Simpson nodded that he understood. So did Mrs Simpson.

There was no dessert. There were second helpings if the Simpsons cared for it. The other diners, Mr Simpson noted, gave no thought to it; and he did not wish to appear insensitive. The room was abuzz with laughter and had recovered the high spirits of earlier, when the Simpsons had found themselves alone, outside. The 'couples' wandered around the two tables. The women presented their men who were embraced, their faces held and kissed on both cheeks.

They were deserters from the Russian Army. Soldiers in the last regiments to fall back from occupied Germany in the late-forties. Men impatient to be with their girlfriends, their wives and families. They had fled the Army, only to flee their homeland.

Mr Simpson learnt this outside the restaurant. Maggie was off trying to find a bathroom; and he was enjoying a cigarette when he felt a tap on his shoulder, and the surprise of hearing his name spoken.

'Mr Simpson, please?'

It was the same man who had shown them to their place in the restaurant. Over his shoulder Mr Simpson saw the doors of the restaurant burst open with the exit of a happy laughing couple, and there was a split-second view of the bus driver looking back his way.

The man in the waistcoat was very polite. He meant no harm. But he needed to know some things.

'How did you find this bus tour, please?'

Mr Simpson told him the business of his wife going out to buy ice-cream – how she had returned with the cardboard notice. And the man said, 'Yes, yes,' as if these were things he already knew. He said there was a man, Kolya, and he pointed back at the restaurant. Kolya had a confectionery shop popular with Russian *émigrés* in London. Could it have been there that Mr Simpson's wife had found the notice?

'Look, she went out to buy ice-cream. That's all,' said Mr Simpson. He didn't know anything about Russian deserters. He told the man he was a builder. A successful builder. Then he told him the name of his country, as if that fact alone might explain everything. This other business . . . he shook his hand.

'It is very important,' the man said. 'The women are to travel in the bus as far as Leningrad. From there they will return and the men will carry on. Please, we do not want unhappiness. We wish to avoid mistakes.' The man asked Mr Simpson to show mercy. 'These people are not traitors. They are husbands and wives.'

There were more people than seats on the bus. It was a gay affair. It was pitch-black outside and nowhere did there appear so much as a farmhouse light. Mr Simpson guessed they would be on back roads all the way to Leningrad. He passed on to Maggie what he had been told. He whispered of the people around them who were swaying in the bus aisle, laughing and kissing. Someone had a camera and was taking photographs. Across the aisle from the Simpsons was the same man who had got on the bus in Berlin and who this morning had offered them the carrot. A woman now sat on his lap. He tickled behind her ear, and she in turn gave his nose a playful tug. A Polaroid was passed around. The couple laughed at themselves in the photo. Only in the photograph did Mr Simpson notice the woman's bad teeth. She was laughing and he could see the black pits of her teeth and the swollen gums.

These were people – men and women the Simpsons' age – laughing and crying. There was a jokester among them – a man with a shaven head and twinkling blue eyes who every so often rose out of his seat and shouted something that cracked everyone up at the Simpsons' end of the bus. To the front of the bus were younger faces – young men and women – and

Mr Simpson wondered if they were relations, perhaps even the offspring of marriages forged in newly adopted countries.

Mr Simpson looked at his watch, as was his custom before turning off his bedside light. It was ten o'clock when he sealed his face with a smile, and closed his eyelids. He never really managed to fall asleep. The bus rocked and on corners pitched him sideways. When next he opened his eyes the lights in the bus were out. It was quiet. Maggie was sitting upright, wide-awake but lost in thought. Mr Simpson had to shake her arm to make her aware that he was no longer asleep. He said he would like a peppermint. Maggie felt around in a bag for the peppermints. The rustling of the peppermint bag was unreasonably loud, like in a cinema, and Mr Simpson was suddenly aware of the other noises.

Across the aisle, in the tight confines of their seat, Andrei and the woman with the bad teeth rested awkwardly in each other's arms. Towards the back of the bus, in the aisle, a man lay on top of a woman who still had her shoes on.

Once, many years ago, Mr Simpson and Maggie had made love on the floor of a bach – and an hour later had sat in the same spot with the Ralstons eating a ham salad.

Mr Simpson took a peppermint from his wife, and popped it in his mouth. He noted Maggie's restlessness, a certain look that overtook her face when he occasionally breached a rule of etiquette, and wondered if it was the noise of him sucking the peppermint. Then she whispered, 'Have you noticed?' Yes, he nodded. He had noticed. 'Those poor people,' she whispered. She felt that they should give up their seat.

'For the time being. We can do that, at least,' she said, and she gave a slight nod for Mr Simpson to check the aisle behind.

Two couples were embracing. Mr Simpson reached across to the nearest pair and tapped the man on the trouser leg. The man lifted his foot and shook his leg, and went on kissing the woman. This time Mr Simpson pulled on the man's coat, and was more successful.

A man with grey sideburns and crewcut turned around. He was perhaps a few years Mr Simpson's junior, but he had held and continued to hold his woman like a teenager, both hands around her waist, her crotch pulled in against his own. Mr Simpson might have thought of the time he switched on a light to surprise his daughter with Grant Wicks. But there was no such terror in the eyes of the Russian man – not even surprise. More a patient kind of curiosity. But the woman understood before he did and gave a big smile and a push when she saw Mr Simpson and his wife stand up from their seat.

The Russian man clasped Mr Simpson by the shoulders, and nodded formally. Mr Simpson gave the man a pat on the shoulder. Maggie was smiling happily. She felt proud; and Mr Simpson knew that part of that pride was for himself. He knew he had done something that his wife would never have expected him to do.

'Hold me,' she said. Mr Simpson did what was asked of him. Mrs Simpson put her hands against his chest, to steady herself, and then rested her head there. They stayed like that for a few minutes; then his wife looked up. She wanted him to kiss her. Mr Simpson wiped his mouth with the back of his hand, and cleared his throat, as if he were about to deliver a few words, and kissed his wife.

'That was nice,' she said, and put her head back against his chest.

Mr Simpson was watching the Russian couple making love on their seat, and he was wondering what he and Maggie would look like. He watched the heave of the man's body – and the woman's mouth open to catch bubbles of air. The expertise in the man's limbs caused Mr Simpson to wonder if he would appear the same, and whether after such a long separation from Maggie he would be able to restrain the greed of his body, and how could one sustain the greed without the separation?

Once he had thought about leaving Mrs Simpson. It was after the birth of their second child, and Mr Simpson had started to think about other women. It turned out to be a passing thing. And, of course, he had never told Maggie. Now he turned his thoughts to the young faces in the front of the bus. And as he watched, he wondered which life the Russian man was thinking of, at that particular moment.

All of a sudden the motion stopped. The man's head fell to one side, the woman's eyes opened, and smiled at Mr Simpson. Maggie crouched down and scratched around in her bag until she found the bottle of Vitell. She poured a cup and handed it to the woman who had to reach over the man's shoulder to receive it.

'Spasiba,' she said.

The man whispered something, and the woman said in hesitant English, 'Thank you.'

She kissed the man's forehead, and gently pushed him up, and as he reluctantly rose he pulled up his trousers, and the woman flicked her coat over her legs. She slapped the seat beside her, rose, and said something in Russian. The man agreed.

'Yes,' he said, and, nodding at the Simpsons, gestured to the space left behind.

Mrs Simpson laughed. 'Oh no,' she said. Then she smiled up at her husband. Mr Simpson rested a hand on his wife's hip. The other couple moved away. The man patted Mr Simpson's cheek with his hand. Mr and Mrs Simpson resumed their seat.

'I feel so . . .' she began to say, but Mr Simpson cut off the sentence with his lips. For a moment he wondered how things would appear in the morning, and back home, what he and Maggie would tell their friends. Then he felt inside his wife's coat for her breast, and discovered the nipple ready.

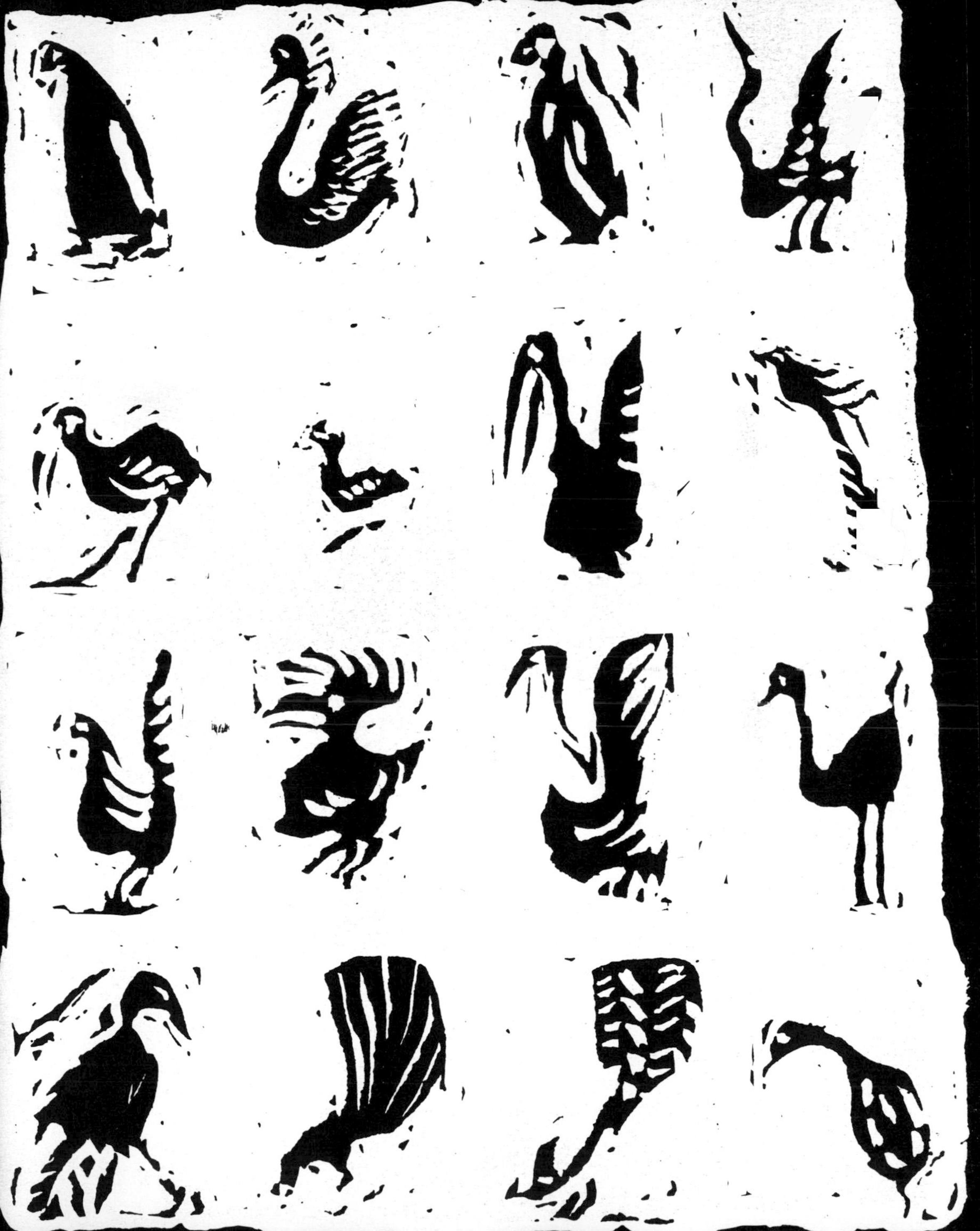

PADGETT POWELL
Wait

Spavined, clavicular, and cow-hocked, with an air not of malice but simply of a leaden determination that seemed to come up from the hard baking ground itself on which it stood, chained, confined, gravitate to the orbit of earth depressed, moonlike, and polished by its five-foot circular diurnal travelling, looking forward with a low-lidded not scowl or glare but just *look*, the eyes half-lidded and half-rolled suggesting not insolence or calculation or even sentience but a kind of pride – rear-axled and log-chained for a lifetime to a hot powdery hole in which it is its fate to consider its chances of fighting, the rare times not chained, for its very life: a profound self-esteem that says simply, *I am here, you see that I am here, what need to look you in the eye?* – the bulldog bit the corncob truncate.

    – Truncate?

    – Into foreshortened segments, not as if –

    – He busted it all up?

    – not as if they had once been parts of a greater piece, but as if they could yet assemble into a piece larger, so profound was their truncation –

    – Dog bit the corncob?

    – there, vanquished at the splayed feet of the animal with an air not canine but not unlike a locomotive, small, furred, steeled yet without so much a train of cars behind it as the quintessence of linked and smelt earthcore, its log-chain –

    – *Dog bit the goddamned corncob?*

    – yes. Yes. Wait –

    – In *half* or *what?*

    – Wait. Not halved so much as *no longer whole*, as if in the authority of the bite was contained the undoing of natural history, and, if there were two pieces of corncob where there had been one, there might have been now twenty; for the moral, imperative, and inviolate impression made was of a corncob no longer *one*.

    – In half, in the dirt.

    – In the moted, desiccate, rivulet ground.

    – I dig where you comin' from, but you talkin' in circles.

    – Helically, gyring, for the truth is never at one location but variant, even unto itself; dislocate, inchoate, rubricate or subtler chance –

– God, man. *Say* it. We this far, all happen is dog done bit a corncob. I'd have me a dog done kill a horse by now, drag a man out a burning house. And you want you a mean bulldog? He gone bite a *corncob*? Shih. I seen dog so mean he bust up his water dish – a Buick hubcap! And not just once, every time you give him water. Don't even *drink the water* first! Whyont you let your dog bust up a bicycle with a kid on it, or bust up lawnmower, a *runnin'* lawnmower –

– The corncob is integral to this kind of story. You can do a lot with a corncob.

– Yours is bust up.

– True. You can do a lot with what can no longer happen. Thwarted fate is integral to this kind of story.

– Well, integral some action in your story. Git on wid it.

– Wait. Wait. Wait.

– What else I can do?

– Wait.

117

South Carolina

On a low-country plantation, where I am invited but do not belong, there is a group of young women dressed up and going to a ball, or cotillion – if that is the word, and I doubt that it is – or even wedding at another plantation, as happens here: you frequently go to one party in order to prepare for another party. They are in white finery that looks to me bridal but probably is just formal. One of the women is *striking*. She is rather small, compact, tanned, her hair back tight – she looks like an accomplished horsewoman in an evening gown; a bit out of her water but not unhappy about it. She and the other women are heading out, a bit cattle-like, stragglers and strays but in the main accomplishing the harried exodus. I catch her eye. There is no time or place for introductions. I go up and suddenly take her by both hands firmly: 'I'm quite unlikely ever to see you again.'

'I've *got* to go,' she says, pulling away, it seems with only one hand, her right, which has three rings, I notice, on one finger.

'Well, put a glass slipper in the red pickup out there,' I say. She leaves.

I go to the bar. It is in a large card room with a commercial big-screen television in a corner. The low-country boys do things *right*.

Someone says, 'Hey, man, she's married.'

I shrug. I am confident I acquitted myself brilliantly. The motif is backwards – my pickup truck among the Mercedes is the pumpkin coach, and I should have on the slippers – but, I think, that is even better. She'll get the picture. The backwardness is a profit in irony.

At the bar I am served a beer and a parrot. You may have a parrot for your shoulder as you drink. The parrots, when served, lie on their sides on the bar, perhaps talking to you, until you pick them up. They are stored on a shelf under the bar like silverware and either can't immediately move or are trained not to.

SIMEON DUMDUM JR

Two Poems

Why There Are No Cats in the Forest

A parrot was what
he once had on his left shoulder,
the thought of it,
which came long before
the actual bird
which never came.
It never came.

It was never the season
for parrots
which were unreachable,
which nested on the highest
and deadest of branches
of the tallest tree
in the farthest forest
and he lived in the city
and no one ever promised a bird
or spoke to him.

And the reason he was now carrying
a stray cat
on the same shoulder
was that the thought of the parrot
would not fly away.

A dream never flies away
but it can be destroyed
or eaten.

Afternoon in Cataingan

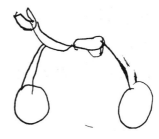

A store. Inside, an old woman
Offering another a leaf of tobacco.
Outside, a parked motor cycle,
A hen near the front wheel,

And further down, discussing the condition
Of a jeepney, stand two men,
One stripped to the waist but wearing
A watch,

And, how often have I seen this,
A dog lies on its back, scratching
Its face with a hind paw
And wriggling.

(The street so empty, so safe, just the place
For an accident.)

Before dark they come, the young men,
One holding an air rifle,
Another the yellow bundle of a bird.
They are stopped by an elderly man
                        with the questions.

Everyone is happy.
The man finds below the wing
The red spot that tied the bundle
Forever.

OWEN MARSHALL
Tomorrow We Save the Orphans

My final voyage, a winter's night, and Dubois accompanies me as a courtesy of farewell. After more than a year at Acme Textiles I have been appointed a researcher with Statsfact Polling Agency. Dubois is piping me ashore. 'I might do the same at your age,' he says. 'But later you'll see the advantages of night work. Fewer people and more interesting ones.' He's right; they drop through the sieve of daylight employment to a nether world. The most fallible of fools and perverse of the profound.

The breath that forms Dubois' words is a plume in the freezing air as we stand beneath the water tower and check the sacking on the pipes. Appearance is most marked and memorable on the day that we meet a person, and the day we part. Dubois' continental good looks are in some way debased; the casual, toss-away features of a circus rouseabout, but his eyes and hands have individual authenticity. Dog-killing hands, strong and supple, with muscle raised between thumb and forefinger, and eyes that will not tolerate deceit.

'I've been reading more about castle development and the influence of the Crusades. Brattices and the advantages of circular masonry,' he says.

I returned from Europe with an innocent bladder-infection and a debt of over three thousand dollars to my parents. Acme Textiles was unimpressed by my education, but when I crooked my arm to make a muscle and talked of labouring in Wolverhampton the personnel manager said OK, I'd got it, night work, but only if the caretaker liked the look of me. I never saw the personnel manager again. He was the Charon who delivered me to the underworld. His name was O'Laughlan. The managing director, whom I never met at all, was called Jim Simm, and the caretaker was N.F. Vincenze Dubois. Life is full of such splendid ironies.

On this last night, a winter round, Dubois seems willing to put aside all except that final cover which is the necessary reserve to keep the glare of other people from our soul. At farewell to comradeship and proximity it matters little if some confidences are shared that might be awkward if you had to meet again. We all learn to jog along in our relationships, not expecting too much, not admitting ambitions we can afterwards be beaten with. 'Have you really been here fourteen months?' says Dubois. He has a muslin cleaning-rag knotted around his neck for warmth and the collar of his tartan jacket turned up against the chill. 'Fourteen months. Fourteen months,' he says. 'And I don't remember more than two or three things in that time, apart from the Middle Ages, that I care a damn about. I hope it's different for you.'

Night has a stark effect. A liposuction that removes the inessential until the bones, the sinews, the organs only of an impartial world remain. The dump-skips cast perfect shadows from the moon across the frosted shingle and dirt of the yard. Larger stones are rising up like mushrooms, and cats troop Indian-file silhouettes upon the wall at Pine Light Engineering with shoulder bones that undulate against the sky. Grass that grows three storeys up in the gutterings gives a faint, prairie whisper in the barely moving air, and hedgehogs fossick out from weed and fennel corners to feed.

Frontages of industry present the latest faces, but the backsides retain the scars and emblems of old allegiances. Pine Engineering was once the warehouse of Pacific Skins Ltd, and Acme Textiles itself incorporates amongst others the bulk of Aldous D. McManus and Sons, Pastoral Agents and Scourers, estb 1862. The brave, old lettering can be seen behind the fire escapes. Dotty Standish has come to one of the small side doors to cry, as she does most nights. Her husband died three months ago from cancer of the bowel. Dubois will not fire her yet, as she has been a good cleaner for several years.

'I could have made you assistant caretaker, or night watchman, if you wanted to stay on, even though you're no good with your hands,' says Dubois as we check the loading-bay doors. Our steps echo on the hollow, wooden ramps and between the echoes is the sound of Dotty snivelling not far away. 'I heard a new dog barking last night,' says Dubois. 'A Labrador, or Labrador-cross, I reckon, at the refrigeration depot, or perhaps further over at the seed driers.'

Dubois is chunky and middle aged, but nimble still. In the main machine room he vaults to the top of the spinners to check them. He leaps from one to the next. There are fourteen French Bavantés and six Wisconsin Hammonds; the names in proud red-and-green bas relief on the sides of the casings over which Dubois strides. He has come to check on the Hinkles' electrician. As caretaker Dubois has patronage to dispense: not just cleaning for the women of his choice, but suppliers and tradespeople. The Hinkles man has finished with the freight lifts, and tells us they should get their certificates of worthiness now.

'I meant to say,' says Dubois, 'that my tele is playing up. The sound cuts out every now and then.'

'I'll call in on my way out,' says the Hinkles man eagerly.

'Would you?'

'No sweat, Jesus, no. If it's anything serious we could let you have a nearly-new set we've repossessed.'

'Tell Keith I'll probably need someone out to fit new fluorescent lighting in accounts. I'll know for sure in a week or two.'

'Right. No sweat. See you then,' says the Hinkles man. Dubois conducts the conversation from the height of the spinners, which accentuates his mastery. He now climbs higher as the electrician leaves. Into the steel rafters he moves to check his rat baits, disturbing delicate colonies of wool fibres built up over years. Some lightly fall in clumps like varicoloured lichens, others disintegrate and drift for a time before the lights as a haze of green, or gold, or blue.

'The bastards have been at it.' His voice is tight with satisfaction. 'Oh rat, rat, you'll feel thirsty now.' Dubois half-swings through the bolted rafters above the machines, leg and arm, leg and arm, careful to protect his head. 'Rat, rat,' he says, 'you feel the thirst of death.'

The factory at night is a Titanic; dimly lit and throbbing. A place of many levels and decks, with lives a world apart separated by just a bulkhead, or a narrow stairway which says: FACTORY STAFF ONLY. The boiler pipes are never silent in this season, the air-conditioning fans resonate with individual melodies from deck to deck. A persistent vibration gives a sense of movement, of voyaging, so that Acme Textiles is pressing on over the sea of the night.

Vincenze Dubois is more absolute captain of the firm by night than Jim Simm ever is by day. In trading hours the place is subject to the compromise and transactions of the world, taking cognizance of powers of equal, or greater, strength. But Dubois has a concentric empire: a ship of the night that rumbles self-sufficiency and to which only minions from the outside come. This caretaker knows the place as an extension of himself. The cleaners and the routine of their tasks, the machines in all their variety, rat paths in the ceilings and cellars, the seventh skylight in the warehouse which leaks after hail. He knows the stalagmites of borer dust glinting on the lower beams of the acid store, the folded blankets behind the dye crates where the works supervisor takes Sarah from reception during breaks, the blue pigeons that have pushed past the netting on the east gable, the forgotten box of Chinese silk cocoons above the cupboard in the old Board Room presented by a trade delegation in 1949. Dubois knows Stevens of personnel picks his nose, that the three original doors nailed shut behind boxes in the old storeroom are pure kauri, that the morning sun strikes Acme first on the rusted iron above the blue-pigeoned east gable. There is a piebald rat in the boiler house, Dubois tells me, which eschews all poison, and antique-green jars in wickerwork ignored beneath the dust and spiders' lace of the upper gantry. Cannington writes old-fashioned poetry on the firm's paper, and Tess Eggleslee hides stolen lipsticks in the ledge above the toilet cubicles. There is a faint stain on the smooth wooden floor of the press room. Dubois points it out as the blood of Kenny Donald crushed there seven years before by a fork-lift carrying the umber bolts of commercial grade which were so popular at the time.

'Remember we talked of mead,' says Dubois. 'I've had some working; several batches, in fact, with different herbs, but it's difficult to control the fermentation. I'm not very hopeful and honey's bloody expensive.' We are in the first-storey offices which have imitation wood-grain Formica desks and vinyl swivel chairs with corrective backs. There is not a cobweb, or a textile thread, in sight. From these windows the freight yard is a bleak field. In the summer the security beams suffuse the penetrable and billowing air, but now their light is fractured, crystalline in the frozen night. The Tuki sisters watch Dubois check behind the wall heaters and beneath the photocopiers.

'You won't find anything there, aye,' they say.

'I'll catch you one night,' says Dubois.

'Promises, promises,' they say.

Dubois will miss the medieval age I suppose. As well as women and machines, he likes discussion of the origin of heraldic devices, and how *donjon*, Norman-French for tower, became corrupted by time and usage into dungeon. Dubois likes me because I am an intellectual and simpleton. I am without authority or skills in the nether world, yet have information he finds interesting. 'There was a Dubois with William at Hastings,' I say, 'and Cardinal Dubois was Premier Minister in 1772 and in effect the ruler of France.'

'I was told that Dubois meant by the wood. My grandmother always said we had property in New Orleans.'

'Edmond Dubois-Crance served in the Royal French guard, but became a leading Jacobin in the revolution and organised its armies.'

'There's a negro branch of the Dubois in the States,' Dubois says.

'What did you do before?' I ask him.

'Before?'

'Before becoming a caretaker,' I say. Dubois leans away from me to peer behind the drink dispenser.

'Charlotte, Charlotte,' he calls, and Charlotte comes from one of the corridors. 'There's cardboard cups squashed down the back here. Get one of the girls to poke them out with a broom handle, please. Michelle, perhaps; she looks as if she'd be better with that end than the brush.' Charlotte laughs, nods, walks away; says nothing. 'Charlotte,' calls Dubois again after a little while. He has found something else to rectify, but Charlotte is out of earshot. 'Charlotte? Ah, never mind. Do you ask a lawyer or an architect what he did before? Do you ask a headmistress or a mercantile banker what they did before?'

'It's just that —'

'It's just that you can't imagine an eighteen year old deciding to make a life-career as a custodian, right?'

'No, it's not that,' I say, but it is exactly that. Caretaking is something that you end up doing, surely, as a result of compromises and expedients. A wintering over until you line up something more in keeping with your view of yourself. There is something in the concept of caretaker that suggests the pathological poles of murderer or poet.

'It's my life's job,' says Dubois. 'I started out as a primary-school caretaker and I've done pretty much all sorts. The more night work the better, though, because I'm interested in freedom, see, which is a form of power.' Dubois hears a car in the alley, and leaps up on to one of the canteen tables so that he can watch the lights pass his domain. We can hear the car back-firing as it slows to turn into Astle Street.

Charlotte comes in to release *The Phantom of the Opera* in volume from the cleaners' transistor. The Tuki sisters, three doors down, start to sing along and, before Charlotte can go back to work, Dubois begins to dance with her. How well they dance on the white and yellow of the cafeteria floor, amid the chair legs upturned on the tables, and spun by the swelling music of the night. Dubois is handsome and the muslin cloth a cravat at his throat. There is no parody in the care and skill he shows, and Charlotte's calves are well muscled above her working shoes. Faces and voices at the doorways as the other women watch them dance, and when it is over they go back to work the better for it. Dubois is unselfconscious about the life he leads.

On our way to the boardroom, Dubois and I are talking of tallage and the earliest practice of paying in kind. And the poll tax which was a further burden on the serf. The boardroom has BOARDROOM in gold pretension on the door, in case there may be confusion with other rooms with a fourteen-berth, pale pine table and better-than-average blue vinyl chairs. Dubois smokes a black cheroot, but we don't sprawl, for it is too cold in this part of the building.

Our hands are in our pockets and we shrug our shoulders for warmth. On the wall there hang the managing directors: Jim Simm will be added in good time, but their *doppelgängers* of the night persevere only in the minds and hotel-tales of casual workers. Even Dubois can remember only the caretaker immediately before him. A Twenty-first Battalion man whose stashes of gin still turn up from time to time. However complete and despotic their reign, caretakers go largely unrecorded. So earls and barons pass into history by virtue of their rank, while butlers who bestrode a world below the stairs are forgotten when their subjects die.

'So heriot was the death tax,' says Dubois. 'Nothing much alters in the state's greed, does it?' I am so close I hear the outside leaf of his cheroot crackle as he draws in and the red rim moves. 'Let's talk of Sir William of Cabagnes who captured King Stephen in battle,' says Dubois, his fingers checking a window catch. I am aware of the subterfuge and interlock of time and place in that instant. The moonlight winking on Dubois' thumbnail at the window, my rather nasal voice pronouncing the vowel in mace, my torso shrunk within the heavy clothes of winter, the words 'Alistair P. Bridgeman' beneath his proud black-and-white face on the wall. A tremor through the carpet from the Phantom's songs beneath. Then time moves with a whisper and again we bowl on towards our end.

The cleaners are nearly finished for the night. The long watch is an exclusively male affair. They walk past us in the shadowed corridor. Dubois asks me to check the fire doors on level three. He'll catch me up shortly, he says, and as I go on he steps out to separate Carol from her friends; guiding her towards the switch room with the pressure of his hip. 'Wait your patience,' Carol says, so as not to seem too amenable while still in view.

The fire doors are as safe as most excuses. I decide to walk back outside the loading bays. Dubois has told me it is important not to become too rigid in one's routine, for that could be exploited by a thief. I doubt for the moment that he is following his own advice. An angel swish, high on the factory side above me a muffled thump, and a mallard drake falls to the frozen dirt and stones of the moonlit yard. I turn a full circle with a sheepish smile to see who has played this joke, but there is nobody. The drake's sleek head follows me. I don't want the responsibility it brings and try to shoo it away. In response the duck rolls on its side, almost like a cat asking to have its stomach scratched, but one wing extends in a tremor of departing life, and in the soft body feathers where two legs should be is only one and a little blood. Something terrible has been happening, hidden in the night.

A car without lights is driving slowly down the yard. The gravel crunches sharply in the cold air. It is only Ransumeen who works for Sleaptite Security. Ransumeen is an idle, moaning sod who has been an insulation salesman, grader driver, post tannilisor, and now despite his complaints will see time out in the security business. 'It's an agony, my back,' he says. He gets out and falls into step beside me, pulling on a balaclava to wear beneath his uniform cap. Ransumeen has no regard for me, but seeks anyone to talk to on a lonely shift. 'It's an agony. Too small for my build. I've a good mind to tell them that I'll have to toss it in unless I get a better car.'

'Right,' I say. Ransumeen has a habit of arriving at the Lintell Street entrance after ten o'clock when the women are leaving. He hopes to entice the younger ones with an offer of a ride home in the security car.

'I could do with a workout for the old mutton gun,' he boasts. But Dubois has warned the women against him, because he considers Ransumeen workshy and unreliable. 'I suppose the cleaners have almost finished now?' says Ransumeen. The balaclava does nothing for his looks. 'That Eileen's got a nice pair on her: a very nice pair.' He sees the women coming from the lighted doorway in twos and threes, and hurries from me to offer them double service.

The full moon this mid-winter night has a round, idiot face. My nose is putty, and all of us are made slump-shouldered by the cold. This stark, dead-duck yard of Acme Textiles has no links with the expansive world in which the same night staff played volley ball last Christmas. On that night the air had rolled languidly amidst us, heavy with the fragrance of the chocolate factory, the wheat silos, metallic cinders from the foundry, the sharp tar and salt from the harbour, and the plebeian scents of weeds along the fences of stained factory yards. I was in charge of the beer and fruit juice from the munificent management, and took it from the cafeteria into the summer night where Charlotte, Carol, Rua, Eileen with such a good pair, the Tuki sisters and the others chased a yellow balloon as their volley ball. It was a mutant version of the office party, or the true one, perhaps, with Dubois as seigneur, myself as squire, in the medieval sense. The cleaners were boisterous and obscene, because they were all female together, away from their families and knowing they deserved better than the treatment they received.

The world is a thousand worlds and our experience of it is determined by the point of vantage. The history of one moment in one place is a thousand histories which are horror and joy apart, men and women apart, old and young apart, worlds of temperament and esteem apart, of education and expectation apart. Our own vision is a lie to the rest of the world which jigs beside us. Eileen and the Tukis had leapt for the balloon into the tar-and-wheat-scented summer night, and Dubois gave gifts of panty-hose purchased from his own wages.

I say nothing to Ransumeen of these recollections. Disappointed in his advances he heaves phlegm in the moonlight, tells Dotty he's not going her way, and complains of the rigours of the job as we head for Dubois' winter headquarters in the boiler room. 'Where is that mad bastard?' says Ransumeen. 'A good Kiwi name, I must say: Dubois. Jesus.' The furnace is now kept going all night. Dubois is there before us, his face cherry-red in the glow of the drip-feed and his hands clasped around his enamel mug as if in prayer. There is a low, wooden form that we sit on, and the great pipes lead off above our heads, each one lagged with sacking held with hoops of tin. This is the vibrating engine room of our night ship and, almost, I can hear the ocean of the outer world surge past. Dubois has made a line of blue plastic binding-tape which stretches between the pipes and dries his jockies, woollen work socks and heavy shirt.

'I've been thinking about the three-field system,' he says, with only a nod to Ransumeen, 'as the means of maintaining some level of fertility in village soil. It's the tie to the seasons, surely, one spring sowing, one autumn, one fallow, that explains its importance in the north.'

'I suppose so.' Dubois is at his most scholarly in the post-coital glow. The fly of his work trousers is still partly undone and the corner of a green shirt can be seen, yet the collar of the one he wears is grey. Ransumeen is a reluctant audience on the occasions when Dubois and I discuss feudalism. He is not aware of any connection between the past and the present; those not alive have never lived. His perception of life is reptilian: he is conscious only of the sun that warms his blood during the day, and the frost that slows him in his night work. He can barely maintain a latitudinal interest in things around him unrelated to his appetites, let alone a longitudinal one in the past and the hereafter. Only the concept of droit du Seigneur appeals to Ransumeen from talks between Dubois and myself in the boiler house, on our rounds, or in the gully of the roof where we have sat on pigeon-blue summer nights.

'So the big cheese of the district could have every sheila on her wedding night?'

'It was a prerogative not often enforced in practice,' I say. Ransumeen doesn't want to know that.

'They knew how to live in those days,' he says. Ransumeen's response assumes I suppose that he himself would have been a big cheese.

The warmth of the boiler room is having an effect. Ransumeen lifts his cap to remove his balaclava. 'There's a bloody vicious Doberman at Fraser's yard,' he says. 'A real goulie-cruncher. The police and our guys won't check anything on those premises.'

'Fraser's. Fraser's,' ruminates Dubois.

'Grocery warehousers, down from the coolstores.'

'Of course,' says Dubois. 'A big Doberman, aye? They have tender feet.'

'A real bastard. He tore the cheek off a boy whose bike threw a chain there. He had to have his arm grafted on to his face for ages.' Ransumeen gives me the thumbs-up so that Dubois cannot see. He knows the caretaker's interest has been aroused: an odd appetite whetted.

'If you're passing again in a couple of hours with a mate who'll take over here, then we could pay this Doberman of yours a visit.' Dubois takes up a stick, and thumps along the overhang of the boiler-house roof until a deadened sound tells him that Pongo is lying in his coats there for the warmth. 'I know you're there, Pongo. Remember that if anything goes missing round here you're for it.' I have never climbed up to the roof to see Pongo, but passed him once in the yard. He is quiet, gingery, and on winter nights creeps up to the boiler-house overhang in Dubois' fiefdom.

As we begin another round, Ransumeen takes his cue to leave. He complains about his car again. The yard lights and the moon make geometric patterns of the skips and pallets, the high building-walls and roofs. All that the day will prove worn and soiled has a bridal veil in the winter frost. How cold it is. Can this be the same ground over which Dubois saunters on summer nights, coming from the staff showers back to his humble rooms by the incinerator? I have seen him with a towel as a skirt, and carrying just his trousers and soap. Parrots and roses climbed on his back: tattoos of green, vermilion and purple. Parrots and red roses while I explained to him that steward was originally 'sty-ward' to emphasise the importance of swine in medieval times.

With Ransumeen gone we check the west doors and go in again. Dubois continues to give me company on this my last night. He is thinking of agriculture again.

'Why didn't they use horses to plough with more?'

'Horses were few in number and expensive,' I say. 'The ox was the draught animal for ordinary people; healthier over its lifespan, giving more work from poor fodder and the people didn't mind eating it at the end of it. The Church then forbade the eating of horse meat.' We talk of medieval stock-practices as we patrol the factory. Dubois stops abruptly to feel the air. Niceties of movement and temperature, which I cannot register, tell that a window has been left ajar. Complacent people think that occupations of little status can have no special skills: that any fool can be a lobster catcher, gardener, or poet. The main cleaners' storeroom is ajar, and Dubois' quick instincts lead him to investigate. There lies Dotty with her head on the orbital polisher and her feet amongst the mop handles. Her thin legs are hairy, and her breath comes as quickly as if she were climbing the Matterhorn.

'She's taken all her pills at once again,' says Dubois, and lifts her easily in the fireman's hold to carry her into the cafeteria. 'No, no, Dotty, there's no easy death for you here,' he says, and gives me the daughter's number to ring. It's not the first time, but the last cannot be far off. While we wait and talk of Agincourt, Dotty moans beneath the drug. Dubois has placed a bag of cleaning rags beneath her head, and she smiles fatuously despite the noises she makes. Dotty's daughter and her husband are ashamed of her. They come quickly. Without thanks to us, or more than angry solicitation for Dotty, they bear her away. 'Poor Dotty,' says Dubois. 'She's about come to the end of her tether.'

Ransumeen blows his horn after midnight, and it is sharp in the cutting air. He is back with a friend who will patrol while we go to punish the Doberman who bit off the boy's cheek. Dubois armours himself with his dog-fighting kit, which I have seen only once before; in October when he killed a roving Alsatian that kept shitting by the boiler-house door. More than anything else he looks like a *samurai*; black breast-plate, wickerwork and elbow-guards. The Orient had a modern feudal age, I remind Dubois. 'Know your enemy,' says Dubois. 'It's the head and hands you have to be most careful of.' He has tubular-steel fingerstalls within his fireman's gloves, and tells us that a fully-grown Great Dane has a bite that will shear three-millimetre aluminium, while a bull mastiff damages mainly by shaking. 'I come crawling for a big dog,' says Dubois, 'but it's me that walks away. Get past the shock impact and the bite, and dogs rupture internally quite easily really. Sudden, full body-weight, even from a kneeling position, is too much for them. Rottweilers are sensitive to that despite their reputation. You see, dogs are not meant by nature to be individual fighters.'

Fraser's is well away, among the newer factories on low-lying ground. Ransumeen switches off, and the car glides down the empty street and up to the gates so as not to antagonise the dog until Dubois is ready. There is a straggling, knee-high mist from the sea, and beyond the street light is a main pylon with its own barbed-wire enclosure. The thick cables droop and glisten between that pylon and the next. From its skeleton, knuckles of insulators hang to grasp each wire, and the electricity crackles and snaps so loudly in the winter air that it is difficult to hear what Ransumeen says in his voice at once ingratiating and confident. 'The mad, mad bastard,' he says. 'No one would believe it, would they?'

Dubois is fighting the Doberman on all fours. Neither of them makes any deliberate noise. The dog has Dubois' left arm in its teeth and shakes its head; wrenches suddenly with an instinct unpleasant to see. All the while it keeps its body away from the caretaker, who shuffles in a circle, attempting to come to it. The sparking of the pylon lines is amazingly loud; the breath rising from man and dog mingles in the broken mist. The fight is difficult to watch because of the many shadows, despite the moonlight.

In the entire time the Doberman does not release its first hold. 'Get the bastard. Stick the bastard,' hisses Ransumeen. His greater animosity is expressed towards the dog, I think. He glances behind to check that the street is empty. Dubois and the dog drag and circle their way to the heavy netting of the inner fence. There Dubois is able to get the Doberman side-on at last and bring his elbow down with the weight of his body behind it. Abruptly a sound like the first, harsh burst from bagpipes. A second time the sound, and the Doberman scrambles lopsidedly away with its head low. 'The bastard's done for. It'll die soon,' says Ransumeen. I see in my mind's eye the duck again; its iridescent head, and the wing fretting on the yard. I hear Dotty snivelling. I tell myself I should have no sympathy for a dog that bites a boy's face.

Dubois gives no commentary on his actions as we drive back to Acme Textiles, and does not at first take off his helmet. It is metallic-blue, with a half-visor that modern helmets have. Perhaps he wants time for his civilised face to reassemble behind the mask. The leather padding of his left arm is bright with the Doberman's saliva. Ransumeen catches my eye and smirks.

We have coffee and brandy in the boiler room on our return. What envy might Pongo feel, only a thickness of tin, and a world, away. Ransumeen tells his colleague how Dubois got rid of the Doberman, but is cut short by the caretaker. Ransumeen's work-mate, who is a keen Salvation Army man, takes the opportunity to produce three glossy, foolscap posters promoting an orphans' fund, and he asks Dubois if they can go up in the staff canteens. It is little enough return for his surveillance, and Dubois puts them aside with a nod, close enough to the furnace to have the flames flicker on the beseeching faces of the orphans as Ransumeen tells the story about the staff nurse and the elephant. It's not well received: Dubois and I have heard better punchlines, the Salvation Army man doesn't like the genre.

'They can't be regular partners,' says Dubois as we watch the Sleaptite couple from the boiler-room door. The moonlight and the frost grip ever tighter, and the world outside is motionless except for Ransumeen and the Salvation Army man squeezing into the small security car. 'There were some twenty-five thousand slaves entered in the Domesday Book,' says Dubois, 'but the numbers gradually diminished.'

'They joined the ranks of the half-slaves; the villeins.'

'The luck of birth meant more then.' He seems to have forgotten the posters, but when I remind him that we will be passing the cafeteria he waves a hand. 'This is your last night as castellan,' he says. 'Tomorrow we will save the orphans.' So the orphans remain in the glare of the drip-feed together with the jumble of *samurai* armour.

We decide to begin through the piece room whose arched windows cast the dense, quiet light of the moon like cheeses on the concrete floor. 'Did I tell you of Hugh the Brown, Lord of Lusignan? A wonderful crusader who was victimised by King John,' I begin. Dubois does not answer me. He is lost for a moment behind the curtain of epilepsy. These *petit mal* attacks come only occasionally, then he picks up again without realising that he is ten seconds behind the rest of the world. Here is matter for metaphysical speculation; the brief loss of synchronisation might in the puzzle of time and events either kill or save him. I saw him have a more serious attack only once, after he came from fighting a schnauzer in the docks, and a fierce, spring hailstorm then blocked the gutterings so that the water banked up, flowed down the walls of the computer room and into the switchboard beneath. We were coming back through the nanny presses, having done what we could, when Dubois began soft noises that were not words, took with the urgency of a lover one of the press covers to lie on as he felt the aura. He sat down and held up the palm of one hand as a sign to me that what was to happen would be over without harm, or revelation, without need of any intervention. Convulsive trembling, harsh breath, the glimpse of a parrot's head upon his shoulder, then calm in which his face was innocent. Soon he had been up again and had taken up his command.

'I find the guilds interesting,' says Dubois. He is bending at the grating of the ducts to check the air-flow. 'Furriers and glaziers; silversmiths and ironmongers, doublet-and-hose makers, glovers, cobblers. They were unions in their way.'

'But including employers as well as workers. Setting up standards of the craft as well as conditions. I suppose more like the Japanese *zaibatsu* than unions on a British model.'

'A personal approach.'

'Things suited the scale of commerce; the scale of population then. The people of London would come out to see their King, or a hanging, quite literally. In William the Conqueror's time London was the size of Oamaru.'

'No,' says Dubois. He slows to consider it.

'It's true. Much of England was forest, and wolves ran in packs through Shropshire.'

'Ah, I can see it,' says Dubois. Our checks have led us outside again and our faces shrink in the cold. It seems that he is going to see the whole shift out with me. He flashes his torch behind the loading-bay door handles. He has put some blacking there as a test of Ransumeen's efficiency. 'That whining bastard's not done a check. I'll have him out.'

Dubois turns to look across the yard. He shows his teeth, and draws his breath deeply in defiance of the temperature. 'This is my weather as a northerner,' he says. 'A people get acclimatised over thousands of years, and function best that way. I can't stand too much heat. A cold day and a stiff wind make something in me stir. I'm at my most alert and ready. I have this awareness of my origins.'

'It's sound enough reasoning,' I say. 'Clear genetic links with environment are proved. Look at those Andean Indians with special respiratory adapyations for altitude, and Kalahari Bushmen who hardly sweat.'

'In this weather my tribe stirs inside me.'

'You might find that you suddenly come out with the words of a Frankish war-cry,' I say. I wonder, however, how the boiler room fits Dubois' hypothesis.

'I'm rusty on the Franks,' says Dubois, 'except for Charlemagne. I remember that he could hardly write.'

'Yet he spoke popular Latin as his mother tongue and was also fluent in German and classical Latin.'

'Tell me something else.'

'The Basques had a rare victory over him at the Roncesvalles Pass. About 780 – no, I can't remember. Anyway that's where the epic hero Roland died.'

This is the trivial way I can be a help to Dubois; some recompense for lacking the skills of a handyman. I owe my job at Statsfact Polling Agency to the Acme Textiles testimonial Dubois provided. The managing director's stationery was from Jim Simm's office, and Dubois asked Noreen to do the typing. Noreen was a cleaner, but had been a secretary before she started having children. Dubois suggested the sentiments and in-house detail; Noreen the authenticity of phrase: 'throughout his successful time with us'; 'it is with pleasure and no hesitation that I recommend'. I liked best of all the part referring to my grasp of corporate sales strategy and my progress in the fast-track executive promotion scheme.

'When he was old and sick, he had to campaign against King Godfrid of the Danes, and as the Franks marched north through Saxony the Emperor's pet elephant, Abbul Abbas, died. It was seen as a terrible omen,' I tell Dubois.

'Abbul Abbas,' says Dubois meditatively.

On our way back to the boiler room Dubois detours through his maintenance workshop, where his tools line the walls. All have blue paint on their handles and are stamped with the letters V.D. to lessen the likelihood of theft. I have accustomed myself not to smile, or pass any comment. Through the cavernous main factory we walk and Dubois is contentedly imagining his poison at work above us. 'Rat, rat,' he says, 'you begin to feel the thirst of death.' So might we all in time, of course.

Furnace-light flickers on Dubois' clothes strung to dry and the orphans who still await a home. The great pipes rumble in this engine room that powers Acme Textiles through the night. It is like this with heaven and hell, perhaps: no spatial difference, just that Lucifer leads the night shift and employs the same means to different ends. Dubois untucks the muslin from his neck, allowing it to hang as a scarf. 'We'll have a last cuppa, then you might as well go. No sense in two of us hanging on till the last.' Not once during this last night has Dubois said that we might meet again; that any possibility for the continuation of our acquaintanceship exists. He is too honest and too worldly, understanding the contacts of labour. We have spoken more of manors and garderobes than our own lives, but then who wishes to be told the details of other people's problems; it is sufficient comfort merely to know that they have them.

Dubois comes out to see me leave. He challenges the winter air with Merovingian equanimity, and shows the white of his eyes at the offensive sound of a dog somewhere beyond the engineering works. His hair is greying, but only at the edges so that it appears frosted like all else around us. Even the flat surfaces of tin or wood have fine hachures of frost; not shiny at all, but feathered almost, grey-white in the moon-and security-light like a blossoming mildew. The puddles by the freight entrance, though, do have a crystal surface, and creak beneath our feet. From illogical habit we stand out from the shadow of the factory, although the lighted yard will be no warmer. 'Things will go all right for you,' and Dubois takes a hand from his pocket to shake with. There is music for this white winter night. Pongo is playing his mouth organ. No doubt he has been kept awake by the comings and goings of this last voyage.

For every place there is the official and accredited view; and for every place there is a reverse of which only intimacy allows knowledge. From our lives we can all demonstrate the truth of that. So at Acme Textiles I leave a population known only by those who must board each night. And Vincenze Dubois is its strange captain.

PHILIP SALOM
At Midnight, When Metaphor Will Have to Do

Of course it's always me you hear
in the kitchen cupboards and then
at my desk under the pearled light
shuffling the glasses after midnight

as if to turn back the ways of angle
and refraction, reflection, all those
mysteries of poetry and optics. Attract
like ouidjie the rotten muse with glass

held just so by one finger . . . you can
make that one hand, a drink of something
strong, preferably. Call it Blindfold,
the latest in cocktails, because

it feels like bullets out there.
Of course it's always me
trying to blast out through the blindfold.
Lines of poems culling the air

of other lines of other poems
and sometimes doing so well the air
empties altogether and one is left
fading ripples, the far-off creak of air

as the last life undertow and froth
passes from my mouth. Remember
nothing. I've felt the blindfold
torn away to show blindingwhitelight

like most overwhelming bullets. And to
gasp at the receiving end of a volley
is as god-thrilling as any life gets.
These little angels have coloured wings

they want in black and white, they want
made sense of. They are blind from beauty
and they're sick of it. See, they ARE
EVERYTHING and they're sick of that.

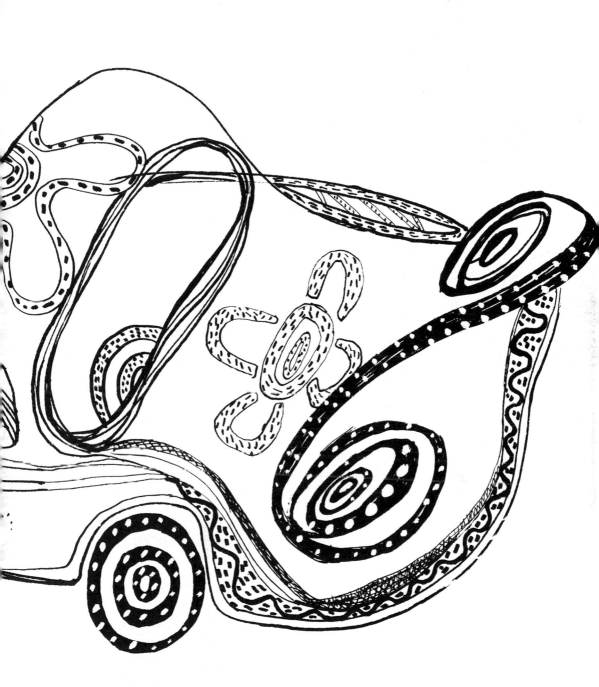

DAMIEN WILKINS
Orders

Daniel Fay has been going through the archives of Our Lady of Compassion Home and is tired of bishops. Toneless, unwavering, lacking in the spiritual – the business bishops, he calls them – the oldest of the letters he handles seem older still than their seventy-five years, in their verbs, drier than the paper they appear on. Humourless dictation. Fay reads them to file them. He's been doing it for five weeks now. A bishop on heating, a bishop on prayer.

Fay's father, Raymond, is upstairs lying unconscious in a bed in the hospital wing of the home. For nearly a month, he hasn't made a voluntary movement. Raymond Fay, stern headmaster on the rise. Mr Fay, Inspector of Catholic Schools. He played golf in his retirement, driving his ball low off a studied swing, meanly down the middle, collecting his tees from behind him. Bulwark against the secular. He counted everything; air-shots, penalties for placement. A stickler. Matchplay against his son whenever a Wednesday suited. Old bugger marked his card like he was annotating scripture. Enquired politely about his son's progress through the out-of-bounds on the 12th. Fay has the scene. Housekeeping, his father murmurs to him on the green in that economical *basso-profundo* – not a sound wasted in his words – someone is keeping our score even if we're not.

That bed, Fay can't take it. He's downstairs in the basement with the bishops. The nuns bring him coffee and sponge cake on a tray. He has stopped asking them how his father is doing since the ones who bring in the tray are not the nurse-nuns, and the reports they deliver are matters of on-the-spot kindness rather than medical fact. He's very comfortable, Mr Fay, they always tell him, cream on their fingers, the kitchen-nuns. Icing sugar or flour on their habits. Sister Margaret. Sister Ruth.

'Just a little spot, right there,' says Fay.

'Oh goodness,' says Sister. 'Thank you, Mr Fay.'

'Daniel,' says Fay.

Fay works the Anglepoise lamp with practised skill, it's like an extra limb. A box with BISHOPS written on its side sits at his feet, slowly filling. Bishop on celibacy. Bishop on tennis. Chalky behinds he cannot bring himself to tell them about when they turn to leave. The coffee black as shoes.

Fay can't talk to his father. He can, but his father can't talk back, and Fay can no longer carry the thing off by himself. He talks instead to Michael Grady, who is in the room next door to his father's, who is as old as his father but not as ill. But Michael Grady can't talk today either. He's having the hair in his ears clipped by Sister when Fay looks in. It's prodigious. All the men are done on a monthly basis. They must grow as much of the stuff as they can just to prolong the delicate, close operation. Sister's headdress falls against Grady's face as she bends closer to the ear, taking the lobe between her fingers and pulling lightly to get at the deepest whorls of white. Fay, at the door, excuses himself. He's embarrassed and returns to the basement for afternoon tea.

He is thinking of his old man. They must do it to him, too, Fay thinks – reach into his father's ears with the tiny scissors. He would like to ask the kitchen-nuns if an unconscious person might still be able to hear such activity. The suddenly amplified snipping. Surely he might. Yet Fay can't bear to ask the same question of the ones who would know, the sisters on ward. He fears they have no illusions.

A plate of pikelets has been placed under the light of the lamp. Fay eats them all. The jam is thick with fruit. He cleans the plate with his finger, then the little jam jar, licks the finger, and uses his handkerchief to wipe his hands.

He is halfway through the first stage of classification of Archdiocesan correspondence. Over the years the material has been stored by the Order chronologically, which is helpful but only a little. Fay's job is to prioritise, accord value, keep what's best and advise for destruction on the junk. He discussed the terms with his father, a week before Raymond, then a resident, fell into his coma, and became a patient. Fay must ask questions of the documents, initiate a working system of placement and retrieval, create a proper archive: founding to present-day. It's your business, of course, his father concluded, your profession. Myself, I am just an amateur. An interested amateur. But when you have a moment, Daniel, I would like to hear. Of course, Fay would tell him what he found.

But Fay's business now feels unclear. His work is out.

The tray moves from beside his elbow. It jolts him from a feeling almost like sleep, a gravity. A kitchen-nun is slipping away with the tray, towards the light coming from the door at the bottom of the stairs that lead up from the basement. Fay likes the singular light-source of the lamp for his work. It focuses him. He sits in a makeshift office of desk, chair and cabinets in a partitioned corner of the large underground area which, otherwise, is neatly arranged storage space. Trunks, cartons, the shapes of old sewing machines

145

and gramophones – he leaves it all in near-darkness around him. A television aerial occasionally glints its needle. Fay believes this nun is new on the job. She lightly kicks at the air in front of her with one foot, her gliding through the stacks less sure than it will be tomorrow.

'Sister –?' he calls after her.

'Oh!' she cries. 'It's Bernard,' she says. 'Sister Bernard, Mr Fay. I didn't mean to disturb you.'

'Daniel,' says Fay. 'And I didn't mean to scare you, Sister Bernard. The afternoon tea was, as always, extraordinary. Thank you.'

'Thank you, sir – the pikelets were Sister Lucy's.'

'Sister Lucy's pikelets have a place somewhere special, Sister Bernard.'

'Your father, Mr Fay – Mr Fay senior, that is – was very fond of them also.'

'*Was*, Sister Bernard?'

'Oh, Mr Fay, I didn't mean, I mean –'

'I'm teasing, Sister Bernard. I'm being silly, I'm sorry.'

'Mr Fay senior is – goodness. He'll be asking for Sister Lucy's pikelets very soon, I'm sure.'

'He will be demanding them, Sister Bernard! Don't you mind me.'

'He will be demanding them,' she says, backing through the door, the light shining off the plate and flashing to Fay across the dimness, the oval of her face. 'Yes, I like that, Mr Fay.'

Fay's slow. He is making mistakes he never makes. He is doing too much double checking. He no sooner finishes a decade than he's back amongst its papers, reassigning worth. The bishops write from the beleaguered sixties. What? Fay wants to know, what is it about this stuff that is getting at him, a professional. Is it that all this correspondence has no . . . *correspondence*? Yet such an idea is beyond his brief. Bishop on hymnals. Bishop on women.

People volunteer their stories. When they find out what line of work Fay is in, they tell him things. He's only an archivist. Sometimes Fay wants to belittle his occupation in this way, to protect himself. It's really glorified freelance filing, he'll say. He works on contract. He visits a company, an institution, a home, for a month or a day, and he hears things. Why? Perhaps these people believe, somehow, that they have found someone at last who can receive their personal histories with the correct degree of attention and, finally, put them in a safe place. He has almost stopped being astonished at what they tell him, astonished at the trivial as much as the major. He's the library of last resort. There is also something of the gloomy latticework and the close air of the confessional about it. He's in a priesthood.

It's fanciful, this notion Fay has, but he has discovered that every day people refuse to die.

Michael Grady's father emigrated from Ireland at the age of seventeen. Fay hears himself asking to see photos. There are no photos. Not of Grady's father, who drowned at forty when Grady was three years old. But of the hotel his father ran down south. The stables he had an interest in. 'There, in that album.' Grady points from his bed to an open wardrobe beside the window. 'There's all me photographs in there. What me kids have left me, that is!'

Fay's eyes, still accustomed to the basement, the steady tracking of one line of black print across a faded or yellowed background of old paper, cannot cope with the unbridled daylight of Grady's room. When he stands and walks to the wardrobe, spots jostle his eyes.

'Bring them over, Danny,' Grady says impatiently. 'Might be something of interest for you.'

Fay collects the album and pulls one curtain across. 'For protection, Mr Grady,' he says. 'Old prints need to be guarded against strong light.'

'Of course,' says Grady, flapping his hand against the bedspread. 'Now bring them here and I'll show you me dad's pride and joy.'

Men in heavy suits and hats standing on a verandah framed by bright sunshine. Grady points them out. Finny McCabe. Tom Duggan. Another fella. Liam Shea. In the foreground, the legs of a child, the beginnings of shorts, the rest of the body lost in the overexposure.

'This?' asks Fay.

'Me,' says Grady and flips the page.

Men in dark trousers, white shirts with suspenders and sleeves rolled, and hats, standing in hay, leaning on wooden gate-railings, and behind the men – in the direction they are all looking – shining in the dark patch of the interior of the stables, the sleek line of a horse's nose. 'Mr Peeps,' says Grady. 'Because he always had a look in.' He pulls the album closer, bows his head into the photograph. 'Me dad's favourite.'

Fay's wife, Anna, is annoyed with Fay for taking the job at the home. Rightly so. He's lost out on his chance for Recorder of the University. It was a nice package. Good holidays. The IBM mainframe. And no one's actually required to work in a university, Fay knows that. Presence is all.

'We can visit your father every day, Daniel,' says Anna. 'I just don't understand why you have to work underneath him.'

But it's not just the job at the home. In the course of the assignment their only daughter announces she is pregnant. Gillian is seventeen years old. No boyfriend has ever appeared at their door. Four months gone, she says that she can no longer eat breakfast. Her skin is very bad. Fay is shocked by the quality of it. Tallowy.

'That's not supposed to happen, is it?' Fay says to Anna.

'None of this is supposed to happen, Daniel,' she says.

'But the eating, Anna? That's not till later, surely.'

'So shall we force-feed her then?'

'Well, what about the – ?'

'What?'

'The one who did this.'

'The father.'

'Him.'

'There is no father.'

'That can't be exactly – '

'Gillian says there's no father, not that she'd want around.'

Fay's trousers are dank and musty from the basement when he comes home at night. 'I rolled in dew,' he tells his wife. Hollow comedy. Anna doesn't respond. He pinches the material, inspects it.

He explains the position to her again and to himself. 'You know why. Dad kind of appointed me. He said it would be a nice gesture. Everybody did.'

Anna goes on with something at the kitchen bench, presenting her back for Fay to speak to. It's a broader back than the one he remembers. More rounded. The sharp line of shoulder has softened, turned over like the lip of pastry on a tin of Dutch Apple Pudding which used to be their favourite. When did they stop having puddings? It seems a pointless deprivation – Fay loved puddings.

'And as well as being gesture, it's business,' Fay says. 'Sister Gwen is a business person. They have an anniversary budget. I'm their man.'

Anna doesn't reply.

'There for anything. Should anything – ' He's lost his thought. Is it this fear of issuing directives that has interrupted him? Fay on love. Fay on family. The subjects he and Anna have been discussing are thinned versions, avoidances, talk deputised by disbelief. Jesus, Dutch Apple Pudding!

Anna, he wants to say, what's she going to do?

Fay's daughter, in the new descriptiveness of her skin – he's seeing it for the first time but how could he have missed it – wanders through the house late at night. He hears her. He gets to her in the kitchen. She is sweating in her sleep-walk. Fay guides her back to her bedroom where, obediently, Gillian gets into bed. He tucks her in, and his hand, moving over the blanket, inadvertently traces where her stomach pushes up a small mound. Fay gasps. His daughter's novel features are set in a glossy inflamed smile. He catches himself trying to return the smile, working up only a kind of grimace before realising, with a feeling of relief which he can hardly admit to, that, of course, Gillian is not smiling at him; she's away off somewhere by herself.

They do not talk about it, he and Anna, though Fay knows his wife is awake when he returns to bed. He does not say he is repelled.

Bishop on climate. Bishop on climate. Fay eats voraciously without appetite. He stays later and later in the basement. The cabinets idle. The good sisters bring a supper of pumpkin soup with croutons. Fay picks off the croutons with his spoon and when he's finished them, bringing the bowl to his lips, he measures off the soup in one continuous swallow. He eats a plate of scrambled eggs, the sprig of parsley he pulls at with his teeth. He follows it with a pot of tea stewed the colour of teak.

From the phone upstairs in the corridor Fay calls Anna to say he'll be late again tonight. She doesn't answer him properly, makes a noise. He cannot be sure whether it's deliberate – Anna punishing him by being difficult – or she's just tired. They've had very little sleep lately. It's after nine already. The residents in the home will be in bed by now and Fay can hear his own voice travelling down the silent passage. He whispers to Anna. She says she can't hear him, what's he saying? Fay's afraid to wake people. His father is just down the end there – which is a crazy idea, he knows – but still he doesn't want to be heard, he doesn't want to take that chance.

'How is she?' he whispers again.

'Who?'

He puts the phone against his chest. Completing sentences. Why is this so hard? Gillian, he has to say. Gilly, they need to shout. But the name's wrong now. It's childish and affected. And Fay no longer knows the codes, the charms. He is stricken with a feeling of exclusion, as if he has been bumped from the inner circle, Anna and Gillian in cahoots.

How is everyone?

'Pardon? Speak up, Daniel. What's going on?'

Fay can't speak. He is remembering a terrible moment from a few days ago; a conversation with Anna about their daughter. How he had slipped so easily into that bureaucratic sentence: I will *make time* to talk to her.

149

Finally, he hears Anna's voice on the phone: 'Do you want dinner saved then?'

'Yes,' says Fay. 'Yes.'

He hangs up the phone but before he's replaced the receiver he hears the line click off at the other end.

Sir Baxter, the big red. The mare, Queenie, with Grady as a boy rubbing down her glistening flanks. Mr Peeps in the winners' circle at a little track somewhere too small to have a winners' circle, with jockey and sash. Grady tells Fay it's little Billy Halrahan aboard. Rode a thousand winners, buried two wives, or was it three? Billy couldn't hold his drink on account of his size. Lots of jockeys being alcoholics before they've hardly had time to hang up their silks. Billy loved Mr Peeps and was his favoured rider. Cried like a baby when he went to stud. Mr Peeps, that is, went to stud, laughs Grady, not Billy! But Fay is already asking of the next picture: Who's this?

Fay finds Grady sitting by himself in the television room watching horseracing. It's Saturday afternoon. Fay has been coming in on weekends to eat alone. The house is oppressive. Gillian no longer comes to the table. Anna reheats. Bishops dictate.

Grady has the first leg of the double and is on At-a-Lad in the second. Sister Bernadette runs his bets. Ten per cent of winnings to the Order. Grady is much stronger now and hates to be in bed, not like 'those lazy, old fellas'. No offence intended about Mr Fay, Grady explains. (Grady always calls him Mr Fay. And it feels right – Fay himself thinks of his father as Mr Fay.) 'It's not as if Mr Fay has much choice, eh, lad? Always one for the circulation, your dad. For the upstanding! A dab hand at posture, he was. Always gave me good tips on – what's that they call it in them fancy places – *deportment!*'

'I think you carry yourself very well, Mr Grady,' says Fay.

'Oh, away with you, boy, all I'm worried about is me poor horse. How well's *he* going to carry himself, what with all that weight. Wish your dad could give us a tip on that, eh, son!'

Fay sits with Grady, watching the interminable build-up to the race, the horses listed several times, summaries of the jockeys' careers to date, track conditions, the draw of the rail. He's anxious for it to start. The spread of odds is flashed on to the screen once again; rows of numbers in lights. At-a-Lad has dropped to third favourite, Jimmy Cassidy on Superimpose, a little over even-money. Cassidy looking for his fourth win of the day. The cameras pan to the favourite. 'That's the one,' Grady says. 'Kiss the double away, Danny!' The jockey bobs in his mount and talks into the ear of the horse as a red-uniformed steward on a big mottled grey leads them towards the gate.

Fay asks, 'How much, Mr Grady? What do you stand to win?'

'Ha!' Grady snorts. 'Few hundred. Pay for me next holiday in the islands, son! Goodbye to that!'

After so much waiting – several horses refuse to go in and must be blinkered – the race is on with a suddenness which Fay had not imagined. For a long time – though it must be a matter of thirty seconds or so – he can't tell anything from the mass of heads and riders, and the drone of the race-caller which seems to run all the names together, unhelpfully listing the field from front to back, then working to the front again. Fay's eager and feels thwarted. He watches the spray of grass and the cloud of steam accompanying the horses.

'There he goes,' says Grady.

'Where?' says Fay.

'Red cap. Four-wide. It's him, he's got them.'

'At-a-Lad?' says Fay. 'It's At-a-Lad?'

'Superimpose.'

Fay bangs the arm of his chair. 'C'mon, At-a-Lad!' he calls to the screen. 'C'mon, boy.'

The commentary is now full of Superimpose. Superimpose by two lengths. Superimpose at the turn. By three, Superimpose.

'At-a-Lad,' says Fay, his teeth tight.

Grady hasn't taken his eyes from the screen. Fay glances at him. The old man seems to be sweeping the field, painfully alert, his lips moving soundlessly as if in some private calculation. Then, very quietly and firmly, Grady says, 'At-a-Lad.'

'At-a-Lad,' repeats Fay.

'At-a-boy, At-a-Lad,' says Grady, louder this time.

'At-a-*lad*,' says Fay.

'Wo, wo, wo,' says Grady.

'At-a-Lad?' says Fay.

At-a-Lad it is, coming from the bunch, his jockey low and forward and not using the whip, moving easily. Superimpose looks stalled in the lead. At-a-Lad's head is now level with Superimpose's saddle. Cassidy checks at his ankles, then starts up a windmill with his whipping arm. They are fifty metres out. The caller's voice has risen to a shout. He is repeating the horses' names with increasing urgency. Superimpose! At-a-Lad! At-a-Lad! Superimpose!

'At-a-Lad!' Grady yells, rising from his chair.

'Yes!' cries Fay, on his feet now too. 'You beauty!'

'Friskeeee Paaahrince!' shrieks the caller.

'F-f-f-f –?' says Fay.

And it's true. At-a-Lad has pulled Frisky Prince, a complete outsider, from the bunch with him, the second horse travelling in his wake, and now, in a blur of whipping, both horses have come up to Superimpose. Three-wide, as one animal, they pass the finish-line.

Grady and Fay collapse back into their chairs.

'Photo,' announces the caller's wrecked voice. 'Two, fourteen, and number ten. Photo.'

After a brief shot of punters applauding – the members' stand is on its feet as the horses start returning through the gate; the women, holding on to their hats, wave white gloves, raise glasses of bubbly; the people at the fence looking slightly dazed, check their tickets – the television cuts to commercials.

'Gosh, why do they do that!' says Fay, angry they haven't stayed at the track. 'Who do you think's got it, Mr Grady?'

'Who do you?' asks Grady.

'At-a-Lad, I hope,' says Fay. 'Of course, At-a-Lad.'

'Well now, son, that's all very nice,' says Grady, patting Fay's arm, resting his hand there. 'But I'd be surprised.'

'How's that?' Fay's a little hurt by Grady's defection.

'OK, look at it this way, son, and I've been around tracks most me life. The horse coming from behind will always be finishing fastest, stands to reason, don't it? And that Frisky Prince, well, don't he deserve the win, eh? Let At-a-Lad do the hard work, went with him beautifully. Up front, young Jimmy did everything he could. You see that, how Superimpose pushed 'em way out. All he could do, see? Horse had nothing to give, so it's tactics, riding. Jimmy's job. At-a-Lad's in the sandwich, Frisky Prince is run the farthest. Who's got it, then? Whose nose? Who has the longest nostril! I tell you, Danny, me heart and me wallet on this one is separated!'

They come back to the track.

'Result of six, race six,' says the caller's voice and a hush comes over the crowd. Fay hears it on the TV. Suspension. Inside, too, he can feel his own hush. Somewhere deep within him, risk and potential and action held by one stilled frame. Grady's words seem right. Fay's convinced they are right. It's the pressure of Grady's hand on Fay's arm which seals it. The surprising lightness of its force.

The result is through now. It confirms not only Grady's analysis, but also Fay's faith in the other man. And Fay hears it as if in the clarity of a dream he is receiving a blessing. This is progress, he believes. It's the first time in months he's been right.

Gillian teases the wrapping. Pokes at it. She's not sure. Anna looks on. Fay nervously watches them both. The mood is awkward, not quite sullen, but tensed.

'What is this?' Gillian says.

Fay notices that, under the full glare of the kitchen light, the peculiar lustre of his daughter's injured cheeks has intensified, the face now overexposed, naked. Hey, he wants to warn her, shouldn't we cover you up? The light has robbed the room of its corners and is just too bright, he thinks. He should have waited until evening to do this.

'Mum?' says Gillian.

'I don't know,' says Anna. 'This is all your father.'

'He's not saying anything,' says Gillian.

'Well, open it,' says Anna.

Fay watches his daughter feeling the package.

'It's chocolates,' she says. 'I can't eat chocolates.'

'Open it,' says Anna.

'You,' says Gillian, offering her mother the package.

'Don't be silly, Gillian,' says Anna. 'It's your present.'

'If it's food, I can't eat it.'

'I'll eat it then.'

'So what's the point of it?'

Suddenly Fay feels he's miscalculated. He's usurped something. Or something has usurped him. He should take the stupid present and go back to the home, to Mr Fay senior, lying very still and solemn. To the good sisters. To Grady. To supper. To the cool shadows of his basement, where he has recently come across letters not twenty years old which tell the story of the incarceration by the Bishop of a group of renegade seminarians. They had, with an eagerness too insistent upon itself, sought material for discussion in the Church's teachings on sexual matters. There was nothing to discuss. The young aspirants had been locked in a dark room for two days, with no diversions, the Bishop warned, but their own souls. And Fay's sympathies on reading the correspondence – he now remembers and admits to himself – had gone *instantly* to the Bishop doing the incarcerating. It was perverse, he knew it. If he felt anything for the seminarians, it was envy and anger at them for not seeing their own luck! To have such a place in which to make a retreat! To be so directed! He really believed they'd made on the deal. And it is to this image of cowering introspection Fay now wishes to return. But Gillian rips the wrapping away and it is too late.

'It's a book,' says Anna.

Gillian reads: '*Name Your Baby: A Dictionary of First Names.*'

'Oh my, Daniel,' says Anna. She puts her hand to her mouth.

'Yikes!' Gillian says in mock horror and lets the book drop from her hands to the floor.

The three of them look down at it for a while.

Then Anna bends and picks it up, opens to a page. She studies it for a moment, licks her fingertip, then turns a leaf, flicks back, skims forward a few more pages. It's agonising for Fay. He is almost ready to leave the room. He can't bear not knowing what comes next.

The hesitation reminds him of those Sundays at Mass when some poor sod, having climbed into the pulpit, discovers he has lost his place, and stands up there in front of the whole congregation, scanning chapters almost *idly*, now it seems such a hopeless task to ever find again today's gospel.

Fay remembers the taste of the pew; as a boy, sucking its varnished wood beneath his bowed head and clasped hands. Toffee, lemons.

He remembers his father, moved on one occasion to help out the stranded reader – to the horror of his son beside him – taking it upon himself to begin the reading from where he sat. A voice that instantly fills the church, has no hesitations or clearing coughs but is to the business at hand immediately. A voice that makes the priest pull his chin off his chest and shoot a look at the altar boys to check whether Mass has moved on and he, the celebrant, has somehow missed his cue. And Fay, infinitely diminished by the largeness of the sound beside him and all around him, yet also curiously lifted towards some position of pride in the man sitting so close their thighs rub as the booming sentences strike the high wooden girders in the roof and rebound like hammer-blows, remembers wishing he could disappear that instant – the boy is dying from embarrassment, after all – but he is also aware of a longing for obliteration which is *joyful* in its urgency, so that, finally, Fay begins to ride the sound, becoming at the same time nothing and of-a-piece with the voice.

But Anna's found it. She has started to speak. She begins reading in a normal reading voice: 'Bill. Bird. Birdie,' she announces, then pauses.

Fay waits in the gap. The voice hasn't the expected weight, the force he was remembering from church, but it is enough; he has the inkling of something here.

'Blair. Blanche. Bliss. *Blodwen.*' Anna smiles.

Fay concentrates, not just on the words themselves, but on the relations between the words and on the way the words are settling in the room. He believes he might be getting the rhythm of it.

'Mum,' says Gillian.

And this one word of Gillian's – this 'Mum' – has entered the field, so that Fay must stop and begin again with the new possibilities of sequence.

'Blossom! Blythe! Bob! Bonita!' Anna says, louder.

And with a small crack in the sound of the word that might be the beginnings of a laugh – though Fay still needs more to be certain – Gillian says, 'Stop!'

Go! Fay says to himself, intent on the call. Away on it, now! All of you!

Anna already has the idea. She speeds up: 'Bonnie-Bracha-Braunette-Bree and Brenda!' Almost breathless, laughing, too – there's no doubt now – as she calls them out.

'Aww,' Gillian groans.

Yes! cries Fay inwardly.

She struggles on with further sounds but they remain mere noise to Fay's ears. He's desperate for more. What's the hold-up?

Anna's laughing too hard to continue reading. She pushes the book at Fay. He snatches it from her.

'No!' cries Gillian.

Fay scans it wildly. He's too excited to see how the letters that run across the page make any sense. It's all pace he's looking at. It's a beautiful mess and it terrifies him. There *is* no order.

'Oh, stop! Dad, please,' says Gillian. 'No more. I'll embarrass myself.'

The sweet and sour of the church pew rises in his mouth like warm glue. His tongue seems pasted to the roof of his mouth and refuses to let out the words which Fay figures will be there if only he could clear a passage. Words that will – what? – throw open the stable doors! release the seminarians! (Because now Fay's beef is properly with the Bishop – who did he think he was! With his locks and keys and darkened cells. The light in the kitchen, it now strikes Fay, is all footlight, spots and illumination. A show from which there's no hiding and in which Fay is glad, if a little underprepared, no, *unprepared*, for his role.) Words, he knows, that are old and late and clearly not written down in front of him. Lord, Fay prays, if only Mr Grady was here, a seer of horses and courses, a photo faster than a photo-finish, though not seer enough to win his double. But still. That hand on Fay's sleeve.

'Don't!' says Gillian.

And then Fay does stop. He realises he's been running on the same adrenalin that was pumped through early in the afternoon, when the stalls snapped open and suddenly a line of horses had broken for the barrier. It's the race-caller's voice that has been playing in his head, giving his unrelenting rhythms to Fay's thoughts. What if he slowed it down? What if he looked up from the book? What is it that he would see?

Fay looks up from the book. He sees Anna holding on to Gillian's shoulder for support. He sees Gillian, her arms crossed protectively over her stomach, weeping, pained, leaning against her mother. He watches them for a time. Their arrangement like some ancient architecture. Column supporting column. There is a sheen which holds him. Pushes him away. Gillian glows.

He wants to tell them about Mr Peeps, his nose shining in the stables like the silver run of water in a grotto. And he wants to tell them about Frisky Prince, leaving his run till the last minute when no one was looking.

Fay doesn't know quite how to make himself be believed and he doesn't want to push the analogy too far but isn't he, too, Fay himself, well, on some kind of outsider whose day may have come? And what about Raymond Fay, Mr Fay, Fay senior – whose day may have also come? But don't stop there, Fay tells himself, still affected by the race juices in his bloodstream, what about Gillian, a dark horse! Carrying something extra. And wasn't it true she had a rider on board who, once he grew them, would dig his heels into her soft parts like any jockey with his nose in front? So that really, without insisting on it, he wants to add, aren't we all? *Aren't we all on outsiders?*

Fay waits until they're quiet, until there's just giggling, sobbing.

'Briny,' he says. 'Or Brink.'

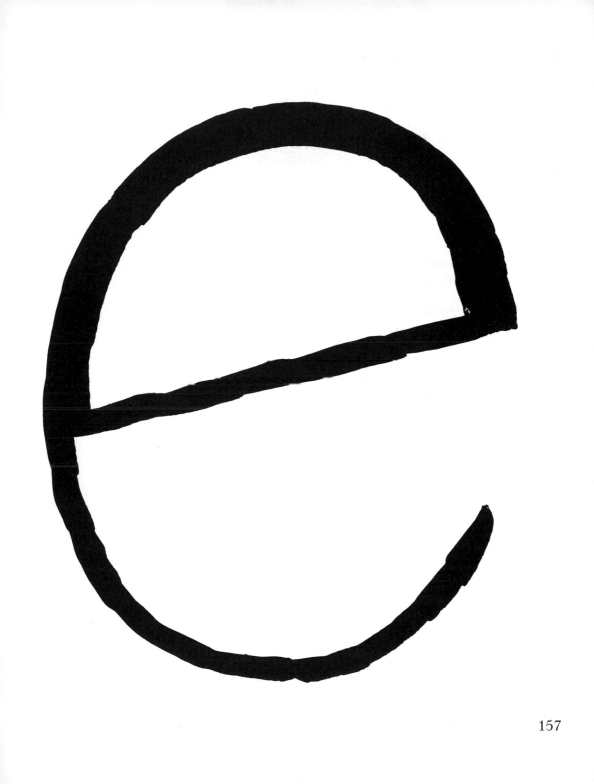

157

ELIZABETH KNOX
Take as Prescribed

'But no one . . . no one in the world could ever seriously believe that I myself did sleep – on that Thursday night in the garden.'
– Isak Dinesen, *Night Walk*

Venice in spring. 10° Celsius. A place where reality has worn thin. The crust of the earth is only thirty metres thick – and undermined by the wells of Mestre. The city has 'a certain slant of light' that 'depresses'. Or perhaps not a slant, but a flatness, pallor, a glassiness. Here, it is said, someone discovered, then lost, a pattern of tessellated mosaic capable of driving men mad. There's a retentive lunacy in the names of its streets: Alley of Curly-Haired Women, Filled Canal of Thoughts – or, more famous, Calle degli Assissini, or Ponte dei Sospiri. Venice – a wasps' nest made of spit and shavings; or a great funeral barge, sailing down the centuries, carrying plague and treasure, heaped around Saint Mark's stolen corpse.

I had been ill with tonsillitis, bronchitis and laryngitis. I had kept my mouth shut about so many remarkable things. On the misty day we walked back from the Villa Borghese I had had to run to catch up with my husband, take his arm, turn him and point to the wolf trotting along the fence line at the boundary of the Rome Zoo. Heavy, levitating Bernini saints; the orange groves on the Palatine hill; the oxen, amphora, grape-bunches on the ceiling of Santa Constanza; or the cold sweat on the walls of the catacombs under Santa Agnese – all had crushed my voice back into my throat. The pain was a stone I couldn't roll away. It seemed it should cost more than air fare and accommodation to cheat winter. The price was my silence. To explain would take only one sentence, but a perfect sentence, nothing broken-backed, one as upright and supple as the small creamy sea-snake I'd seen only the day before, making its way seaward in the canal at Murano.

All this is pathology. I am reporting on the progress of my disease: euphoria, then dread, fever, then a walk along narrow streets turning thirty left-hand corners.

A night walk

I went out the two security doors of the hotel's annexe into the blind alley. For once the windows above me were shut, no one leaning out conversing on either the vertical or horizontal axis. I passed under the black wooden beams over the entrance to the alley and turned left. The street was crooked, broad for Venice, about fifteen feet across. It was lined with Trattorias, Alimentaris, shops selling film and cameras. During the day there were stalls festooned with flags, striped shirts, sailors' caps, straw boaters with long black ribbons, and strings of beads: pearls, pyrites, tigers' eyes, lapis lazuli, coral, jasper, and glass mosaic. The street was quiet now. I passed the church with scarred brickwork, grass on its cornices and a tower full of flat-toned bells, like a head full of cracked teeth. I crossed a canal, left, over the first unadorned marble bridge.

Each turn I took was a door closing securely, biting the air behind me. I entered another broader street, beside a canal. The tide was high; it gulped at submerged steps. A tenth of the solid world was at anchor, in motion, nodding out of unison. I skirted the edge of a piazza, past a stone well capped by a heavy iron lid. The piazza was sectioned by steel sheets suspended in frames – they looked like backstage thunder machines, but were only the city's hoardings brought out at election time for campaign posters. The homeless of Venice, a group of cats, eyed me; dirty tortoiseshells and tabbies with kinky tails, tail-bones showing like peas in a peapod. I turned into a narrow street. Here there was little light – the moon diffused through the pelt of mist that lay over the whole lagoon. The street was very narrow; I could stretch my arms across it. There were narrower streets – like the one two days before that had forced me to close my umbrella, as its spokes scraped the stonework of the buildings on either side.

Another bridge, marble, arched, its steps coated in asphalt. On the corner an ornate iron lamp. Then oddly, growing and dying, muffled by buildings, the throb of a barge's engine. In the next street someone was leaning out of a third-storey window lowering a cat in a basket. The basket touched down and the cat jumped out. The basket was taken up again and the shutters closed. I called the cat, 'Puss, puss . . .' but it looked back at me without comprehension.

I suspected I would find myself walking a loop if I took the next left-hand turn, so I walked on a little further knowing that, doing so, I'd almost certainly get lost. I turned at a corner decorated by a shrine, a painting of the Virgin and child, topped by a plaque remembering some martyred partisans. The shrine was adorned with wilted Easter flowers and two candles, flames guttering in jars filled with red wax. It was another very narrow street. Above, the hand's-breadth of sky was only slightly lighter than the eaves. Then came another canal, a gust of choleric silt, and another bridge, this one not upgraded, the edges of its stone steps worn into ripples, a depression in the middle of each as though centuries of traffic had compacted its atoms.

At the head of the next street there was a statue, a high-relief sculpture of a man, battered, pitted by ice and blanched by acid – and the victim of some home-handyman restoration. Someone had covered the syphilitic hole in the centre of his face with a wedge of tin. The tin was rusted, I reached up to touch it and flakes of rust dirtied my fingertips.

This street brought me out adjacent to a wider canal. I turned my thirtieth corner, went along the embankment, passed a bridge on my right hand. I found myself before a high Gothic arch, a tunnel beneath a gatehouse, and a closed door. The door was ancient, anaemic wood, criss-crossed with narrow bands of studded iron, the studs long ago worn down to nipples. I took hold of the door's iron ring-handles and pulled back, then leaned forward. As I did so the door gave a little on its bolt and I put my eye to the gap that appeared. I saw the stonework of an enclosed passage, a curved wall covered in condensation, side-lit by some unsteady, artificial light – fire, candle, lamp.

Of hidden thoughts, and of heaven

Behind me someone said, 'It's locked.'

I walked out from under the arch. There was a man standing on the bridge. He wore a long pale coat and, at the moment I turned to look at him, the lighted ripples of the canal were reflecting on one side of his face in tigerish stripes. How had I failed to notice him when I passed?

'How do you know to speak to me in English?' I asked.

'By your shoes.'

I looked at my shoes: ox-blood leather, high gloss, with rounded, roomy toes. 'There are Germans wearing shoes like these too.'

'But you don't look German.' He had turned to face me and was leaning the small of his back against the balustrade. Giving me his attention in invitation. I was too timid to come closer.

'So,' he said. 'There's this bridge, and the way back.' He was a native English speaker, but I couldn't place his accent. He said, 'I wonder what you are doing out on the streets in the middle of the night. Venice isn't exactly well endowed with night-spots.'

I had begun to worry about being alone with this man, when a light went on in a window high up the wall behind me. I saw him turn his eyes up to the light, without moving his head, then look back at me with confiding good humour. It was like that electric moment in *The Third Man* when a light goes on and there is Harry Lime, an apparition, smiling at his old friend: *Well, as you can see, you haven't been told the truth.* He said, 'Don't be edgy, it's just a nasty side effect of a very nice prescription – mystery, that is.'

I walked up on to the bridge beside him. The light went off and something seemed to spring back into place around him. Force at rest – that's what it was. I stood beside him, leaning into this invisible volume of being. I looked up at him, he was taller than me, and standing a step higher on the arch. 'I've been sick,' I said. 'My fever has me on a long lead now, and is taking me for a walk.'

He watched me and waited. The shape of his head was less distinct; his movements had pulled some of his long hair free of the collar of his coat.

'I'm leaving Italy in four days.' I tried to explain: 'My white whale is about to sound and disappear into a deep trench.'

He smiled. 'Are you quite sure it *is* a white whale and not a white elephant?'

'I'm like the horse in Caravaggio's *Conversion of St Paul* – sluggish and envious, my eye suspiciously rolled back to watch the man lying at my feet, spread-eagled in ecstasy in a great noontide eclipsing light. And all I'm thinking is: This will never happen to me. I never *wanted* God before. How could I want something I was sure didn't exist? God doesn't exist in the southern hemisphere, but He does here.'

'Sure – He's in retirement in some small villa in Tuscany.'

I shook my head. 'No. He's everywhere here, looking out of the paintings and buildings and the seven separate shades of seven different colours in the sky above the causeway between Mestre and Santa Lucia. He keeps retreating ahead of me, around the next corner.' I pointed at the dark arch, the locked door. 'I'm out walking because I can't sleep. Because I've four more days to find God.'

'And you're afraid you won't.'

'I'm afraid I'll stop wanting to.'

He laughed and I said sulkily, 'God doesn't exist anyway. So I won't find Him.'

'*Should* He exist?'

'I don't know. But this *desire* should. Anyway, I wanted to do something organised while I was thinking, something like magic, so I set out to turn thirty left-hand corners.'

'*Left*-hand? Are you sure it's God you're looking for?'

A clipped-nail moon had cleared the television aerials and conical chimney pots, and was shining its filtered radiance on the canal. Light caught his face in watery flashes.

'On the Sistine Chapel ceiling,' I told him, 'Michelangelo painted God separating light from darkness and casting Lucifer out of heaven. In that painting God, set against the light, and Lucifer, set against the darkness, are the same. They have the same stormy grey hair, the same beard, same clothes. But Lucifer has his back turned and his buttocks bared – you know: *Kiss my arse.* His body and draperies make an eye shape, the buttocks are a cataract-covered iris.'

'I see. Like a total eclipse; really nothing could be more revealing.'

I stroked the satiny marble of the balustrade. 'I have even more trouble believing in the devil than in God. But I'm looking for *something*, something I saw in the mosaic ceiling of the Baptistry in Florence. It wasn't just a *picture* of the time when people believed like I can't, it *was* that time, suspended above ours, like a shell around our world. The realm of the fixed stars they believed in, with the light of heaven shining through its many apertures.'

'Sounds as though you want God's grace. *I'd* rather have a job to do than God's grace,' he said.

'Why are you out on the street in the middle of the night?'

'Look, have you ever heard the unofficial biography of Christ?'

'"The son of a Roman soldier"?'

'No.'

'Tell me,' I said.

The Hebrews had no one jealous God Yahweh, but instead a collection of gods and goddesses. Not that this made them any less ripe victims of Imperial Rome. In a time shortly after the tribes of Israel had surrendered unwillingly to the sovereignty of Rome, a son was born to a couple in Nazareth, an elderly carpenter and his young wife, who was descended by a decayed line from an important Israelite king.

The child, Yeshua bar Joseph, was trained in carpentry by his father. But he was always too restless and enquiring for the trade and was wont to wander off and be found nosing around the libraries of various temples. Really, he was a bit of a disappointment to his father, but his mother doted on him.

In his late teens Yeshua left Nazareth to travel. He drifted around the east,

Babylon and Egypt, Sumeria and even as far as India. Travelling, he made his living by acting and story-telling. Sometimes, when hard pressed, he would court favour, or food, or a bed for the night, by healing people. Generally he was inhibited and secretive about this talent. Whatever his intentions were on each occasion he resorted to it – to pacify some unfriendly locals, or just to take away the suffering of the person in front of him – he could always feel vistas of *future* opening up before him like hungry, uncrossed deserts.

On his journey back home Yeshua made friends with a number of other wandering Jews: a public letter-writer called John; a trio of siblings who sang and danced and collected songs and dances, Mary, Martha and Lazarus; and a couple of actors cum political agitators, Simon and Mark. When he joined these countrymen Yeshua stopped performing his miracles altogether, afraid of setting himself apart from them. They led such difficult, limited lives, his healing made him feel too *able* for their company.

On their return to their homeland the friends settled for a time in Galilee. There they performed to tavern-keepers, fishermen, shepherds, tax collectors, their plays mainly political satires about the concupiscent King and vacillating Roman Governor. Yeshua wrote many of these satires, and often took the leading role. He had such great personal charm that he won a large following of admirers and hangers-on – mostly from the poor and politically disaffected. Although he was loving and frank with all his friends, and with strangers, all Yeshua's friendships stayed on the far side of intimacy. He didn't want to get so close to anyone that they could gauge the discrepancies between him and other people. As it was, when his widowed mother joined him in Galilee, even she – who had held his hand as he took his first steps – could sense the potential power in him. He was like a great rock, balanced precariously on top of a high mountain, surveying the world, camps of friends and enemies, all beneath him.

Yeshua and his friends, fired up by their success in the provinces, decided to go to Jerusalem to perform their plays. Their reception was enthusiastic, but not universal. The King and various priests were thoroughly incensed and wanted the Roman Governor to do something about Yeshua, if not all his colleagues. In an audience with the King, one of the priestesses of Astarte pointed out that Yeshua was a perfect candidate for the yearly sacrifice. The sacrifice commemorated the death of Astarte's lover Atis, who was torn apart by being lashed to the branches of two bent trees. It was the main spring rite in Jerusalem. Yeshua, the priestess observed, was handsome, healthy, reputedly chaste, talented, and a descendant of a royal line. In these difficult times the spilling of royal blood was necessary to mollify the goddess.

On a blazing hot, still afternoon – a Thursday – Yeshua received a warning to leave the city. He and his friends were at the house of a cousin of Matthew the tax collector. Just after the noon meal, the household and guests were sitting about drinking watered wine and arguing politics. A messenger arrived and asked to see Yeshua. The messenger, the servant of a Roman official, was Hebrew, but clean-shaven, Romanised – a young man with his red hair cut short and curling around his brow. The messenger delivered a package and left. Yeshua unravelled the cloth wrapping and found a bag of coins – thirty silver talents – and a length of rope. There was a scrolled strip of vellum with the coins and rope, on which was written: 'Leave the city. These are now the only means by which you may leave of your own *free will*. After tonight I cannot accept any responsibility for your fate.' Yeshua hid the letter and gifts and went out into the walled yard of the house. He washed his hands in the fountain. Its water was as warm as blood. There was a fig tree growing by the fountain, but it had no fruit and cast only a thin shade. Yeshua looked back into the hot shadowy house at Martha speaking while everyone else listened, their robes limp and sweat varnishing their faces. She talked and they listened as though her talk and their listening would change something, as though they'd be recorded and repeated, as though their minds were energy that would neither change nor migrate to another part of the universe. The water dried sticky on his hands and, impulsively, Yeshua reached out one hand and, touching the trunk of the barren fig tree, he cursed it. The blow was casually malicious, but lethal. It was many days till the women of the house noticed the fig was dead (dead leaves had fouled the fountain when a servant went out to fetch water to wash a corpse). They said it was the heat, or the wrath of the goddess at a tree without fruit during her fertility festival.

That night, Yeshua was arrested, taken to the temple of Astarte, and dedicated for sacrifice. But his friends loved him enough to defy the goddess. They talked up a storm in the city's marketplace, raised a mob, broke into the temple, and spirited Yeshua away. They took him to the house of Mary, Martha and Lazarus. The house was in mourning, shuttered and secluded. Lazarus had died of a sudden illness during the day of Yeshua's imprisonment. His family had readied a tomb for him in the valley of catacombs on the road between Jerusalem and Bethany. The sisters of the dead man wrapped Yeshua in the grave-clothes they had washed and scented for their brother. While the servants of the house took Lazarus's body to a secret burial in the Potter's field, Yeshua left Jerusalem in the midst of mourners, on a bier and shrouded head to foot.

The Roman Governor was beset by priests and courtiers demanding that Yeshua's friends be arrested. The Governor was afraid that the riot would lead to more unrest, so he had Yeshua's male friends sought out and taken prisoner. This was a miscalculation on the part of the Governor. Contrary to his plans these arrests precipitated an overnight rebellion in Jerusalem. It was a bloody uprising and the legion suffered heavy losses in putting it down. When the rebellion was quelled the Governor publicly executed, by crucifixion, a number of its 'instigators', including Yeshua's friends.

Martha, Mary and the mother of Yeshua, knowing he would try to return to Jerusalem as soon as he heard about the uprising, shut him in Lazarus's tomb for three days. When they released him they tried to persuade him that he should accept his losses as they did, that his friends were gone and he should look to his own safety. But grief seemed to have driven him insane – grief or the entombment. He swore that, as a healer, he could restore his dead friends to life. With the women he returned to Jerusalem, and stole the corpses off the grove of crosses lining the road to the summit of Golgotha.

They hid away at the house of Matthew's cousin, and there Yeshua tried to restore his friends' torn, sun-blistered, disjointed, parched bodies to life. For a time it seemed he might succeed; the welts faded, the watery blisters melted back into their skin, their wrenched joints straightened. One even opened his eyes. Peter, who was always so attentive, loyal and obedient, opened his eyes and lay all night, trying to focus, idly, like a very young baby. But, at cockcrow, Peter closed his eyes again and stopped breathing. The three women washed the corpses while Yeshua sat to one side (and a servant, fetching water, found the fountain fouled by fallen leaves, as black as rotten seaweed). Yeshua sat, silent, with a cloth over his head. Eventually he got up and, looking at Peter's body, said, 'He's like a hail-spoiled apple; it looks perfect but is spotted with bruises beneath its skin.' He said to Mary and Martha, 'Take care of my mother.' Then he wrapped the cloth tighter around his head, and left the city.

Shortly afterwards a plague fell on the house of the Roman Governor, and spread to the city's garrison, killing and crippling many. The Governor fled, taking with him only his favourite manservant, the red-haired, clean-shaven Romanised Jew. The Governor and his servant carried the plague back to Rome. That summer half the population of that great city perished. All the patrician families were decimated. The empire became bankrupt, the legions rebelled, and Rome fell.

As for Yeshua, he walked out of his life and into a desert. A wilderness of sand and thorns, unplanted, not with the cedar, nor the myrtle, the oil tree, the fir tree, the pine and the box tree together. A habitation for dragons and a court for owls. From that wilderness he went still further, where the dunes crested above him like breaking waves, whose inside surfaces he scaled, defying gravity with his greater gravity. With so much grief, he was a super-heavy body, like a collapsed sun, a starter-kit black hole.

Yes, he walked up dunes like the gold mosaic-adorned domes of great temples, arching and burning above the world he had known. He passed from the Still There, the world of his people, into the Always There, the world of self-made men (but until he came, there were none). And when he had forsaken the Still There he lost something for ever, because, although it was a lesser and sadder order, it was marvellous in the way that skin is more marvellous than sound.

How can I find words to describe where he found himself? And here *I* am, muscling my way into his story looking for words.

I stayed quiet, looking along the canal — around its dog-leg corner a sliver of watery distance, the lights on the Lido, and a lemon-rind dawn horizon. After a moment, sifting himself out of his story, the stranger went on.

In the place his grief and self-disgust and denial of death had taken him, Yeshua grew into the emptiness, into the low pressure, like one of those deep-water fish which swell when hauled up into the air. He grew strong enough to break time and time's desires; so returned to reshape his own life, beginning thirty centuries before his birth — with a world of green meadows, white mountains, dark-blue lakes fringed with frothy white lilies, and with angels. There he began to hoard souls as they left earth, so that one day he could collect the souls of his friends. He made promises to the people of the tribes of Israel, sent his voice through burning bushes and columns of smoke. They called him their God, Yahweh. He awaited his own birth, planning a life for himself in which, this time, the sacrifice would be his, in which he could offer eternal security from death to his beloved friends, in which he would be irresistibly strong and his great love would guarantee their lives.

He sent his mother an angel to tell her she had conceived God — to God. He was born, an infant honoured with gifts and enemies. He was baptised. He spoke words and many believed Him. He healed the sick and raised the dead, came to Jerusalem and quarrelled with the rabbis; turned the money-changers out of the temple. He had a last meal with His friends before the fast of Passover, and He sweated in the garden. He was betrayed, imprisoned, lashed, questioned, mocked and taken to an appointed place of execution and nailed to a cross between two thieves (two bent trees).

Everything had been different. He had lost His own earthly treasure. His friends' lives in the land of the One Jealous God were so different that, when He met them, He would scarcely have known them. Mary, who had been lithe and joyful, was tired and sick with shame when they first met; John and Peter and Simon, all so pious and stay-at-home. They would watch Him as He spoke, their faces reverent and compliant. They were careful not to stand too close to Him unless offering protection in a crush. It was as though they were studying His life, not living theirs. Not that this Yeshua clearly remembered His former life. But He was haunted by sadness, even sitting on the shores of Galilee, watching the coals of the fire crumbling, and savouring the taste of baked fish. And there were times when His loneliness terrified Him – when He faced that cave with the stone four days upon it, His sense of remembered defeat was so strong it had Him in tears.

And Yahweh? Eventually they came to him – the women, the disciples – came to the one who loved them. They gazed at him, their faces wiped clean with peace. They called him 'Father'. They did not know him.

Above us, along the eaves, pigeons had begun to warble, a sound like someone rubbing a pane of glass. I stared at the stranger and he smiled back at me with high good humour, like someone who had won a bet. He said, 'So you see the folly of overextending your reach.'

'If I don't find what I want I'm going to feel like a failure,' I said. 'I'll get on a plane home but my heart will keep on faithfully flying its holding pattern, waiting for a signal from some celestial air-traffic control. I'm more likely to come into money than I am to come into land.'

The water of the canal was grey now, not black, and the sky between the eaves was cream. He had his hands tucked into his armpits and I could see the grain in his steaming breath. 'I don't think I can find my way back,' I said.

His answer was prosaic: 'If we cross this bridge and turn right, we'll find ourselves on the waterfront, I think.'

We walked down the far side of the arch together. He was right. We came out on to the wharfs where the tugs were moored. The sun was rising and the mist turned melon-pink. I looked at him, expecting red hair and a smooth shaven face. Well, his face was smooth, but his hair was black and his eyes dark-blue (but not fringed with frothy lilies, or with angels). We turned right again, towards San Marco, from where everyone is able to find their way.

As we walked he told me, 'Before you leave the city you must go to the

167

Cappella Cortigiani and look at the statue in its porch. It was sculpted by Angelo Santisilia, a Neapolitan, the finest pupil of Leonidas Allori. When his master died Santisilia became a drunken drifter for some time. But he kept his hand in. The statue was his only uncommissioned work. It isn't a sacred subject; but everyone loved it, that's why it's in the porch of the Cappella.'

'Is it in the guide books?'

'I don't know.'

We stopped by the Doge's palace and looked across the mouth of the Grand Canal at the sun on a golden globe atop the wedge-shaped custom-house – and at the domes and decorations of the Salute, its marble crystalline white. The wind was trying to stir the pigeons into the sky and behind us a waiter was cranking up a restaurant's aluminium awning. The man beside me took my arm and, still staring at the Salute as if trying to outface its whiteness, he said to it, 'Loose her; let her go.'

Judas

I stand with my husband in the porch of the Cappella Cortigiani, our backs to the stretched, dusty afternoon sunlight. The statue is on a plinth. It is of a man, down on one knee, his knee and foot level with my mouth. Like the statue of St Jerome in San Zanipolo it is sculpted of white marble flawed by cysts of red. On the shoulder of St Jerome the red marble seemed like liver-coloured birthmarks; on *this* face and bared breast the flaws are blood. Judas – not a sacred subject – is down on one knee, his robe loose. He has just unfastened his rope sash and holds it before him, looped around one hand as if he has begun to make a knot. His head is turned to one side, listening. His shoulders are bent inwards in a cringe, and his muscles are *forced* – upper arms striated, marked by runnels, like the muscles of Rodin's models. He is youthful, his face shaven, his hair in ratted curls. From somewhere above him – the shade of a tree the sculptor has imagined – flowers have fallen; they are rendered, as delicate as carved ivory, one in his hair, one caught in a fold of the robe, and one on his wrist. By his foot rests a deflated bag and spilled coins. There is something about his pose, his furtive distress, his youth, that has made people want to comfort him – his foot and knee have that polished, many-times-touched look. But the coins (the talents) are still sharp and distinct – the spilled money that no one touches.

JORIE GRAHAM
Holy Shroud

Deadwinter our thornberry
   drags in every last cardinal for miles,
its berries finally
   making it pay.
It's never not this way, the clear promise

drifting without perishing into the empty lots
   where they live,
the stubblefields beyond the mall,
   wafting and almost perishing
into the other stenches desolation and cold
   keep crisp,

garment of signals and truths
   winding itself among us – fronds, dread,
sex and fruit – sour milks and the acids
   of tin – drifting, a prayer that matter
is praying, not really ever
   perishing

unless it's bit by bit into such waiting
   as these birds inhabit,
their readiness where one strain of it
   is finally
heard. Now they're lifting as a large cloth would
   into a corridor of sun,

maybe three hundred sets of lungs
   drifting in unison, showering around this single blade
of sun like so many
   minutes.
Sometimes I watch them
   in the back of

the mall, threading in and out of the discarded
   photobooth, necklacing it, trying
to nest in the plexi face-plate
   someone kicked in
after maybe three thousand faces had learned
   their images upon it,

unblinking, pressing,
   the one bit of curtain left
flapping into anything's
   voice. But they fold down again now,
down over the whole
   barrenness, limb by bony

limb, seeking the almost invisible stickiness out,
   making it quiver all over unevenly
with their bodyweights and tiny
   leaps, slipping from still to blur between takes
to keep their wiry claws
   unstuck — oh storyline,

down over the whole barrenness —

as when the face which is His,
   which is not our looking,
emerged (the thing not made of human
   glances) (the thing or moment)
during the night of May 23 18
   94 and Secondo Pia,

having immersed into the chemical bath
   his last attempt at a clear print
of the holy shroud,
   looked down.
The darkroom hummed.
   The negative image took form.
A face looked out at Pia from

the bottom of the tray,
    a face no one had ever seen before
on the shroud, a face
    that was, he said, unexpected. A face. A thing
whose stare overrides
    the looking. He fainted. The print floated

    to the surface of the surface
where it lives now.
    So that when they pulled the shroud out the front
of the basilica
    and held it up, the archbishop's gold robes
flaring the noonlight
    like an hysteria,

when they held it up laid out lengthwise
    on its frame, a large piece of serge linen
covered with stains and lined with
    red silk,

and it took ten people to hold it,
    staring out into the crowd and squinting up,
the sun pressing against the façade like an interrogation light,
    and down into every bevelled cornice,

and down onto the tiny heads and bodies of saints,
    and the tree of life,
and the stone arrows in the stone flesh,
    and Mary on her knees to balance
the composition – When they held it up to us
    we saw nothing, we saw the delay, we saw

the minutes on it, spots here and there,
    we tried to see something, little by little we could almost see,
almost nothing was visible,
    already something other than nothing
was visible in the *almost.*

ELIZABETH JOLLEY
My First Editor

Our headmaster often said he knew which boys and girls would hand in their *Golden Treasury of the Bible* (2 vols) on leaving school and which boys and girls would keep them as a spiritual guide for the rest of their lives.

When I was eleven I was sent to a Quaker boarding school in a small village on the edge of the Cotswolds. Earlier, because my father, in spite of being a teacher, thought that school spoiled children's innocence he took us away from school. We spent some partly profitable years listening to Sir Walford Davies, the returning phrase of the rondo; Commander Stephen King-Hall, parliamentary affairs; Professor Winifred Cullis, germs in unwashed vests (singlets) and milk jugs – on the radio. Wireless Lessons they were called. We had too a succession of governesses from France and Austria. Françoise, Gretel, and Marie. We chased them with spiders and earthworms. And, with my mother, they had *misunderstandings*. They departed in turn, leaning on my father's arm, in tears, to the railway station and the boat train.

The journey to school was always, it seemed, at dusk. My father always came to the station. I remember the afternoons seemed dark before four o'clock. The melancholy railway crawled through water-logged meadows. Cattle, knee-deep in damp grass, raised their heads as the slow train passed. The level crossings were deserted. No one waited to wave and curtains of drab colours were pulled across cottage windows.

My father seemed always to be seeing me off at bus stops or railway stations. He paced up and down pavements or platforms to keep warm. My memory is of his white face, his arm raised in farewell, and his body getting smaller and smaller as the distance between us increased.

The quiet autumn-berried hedgerows, the brown ploughed fields sloping in all directions, and the rooks, unconcerned, gathering in the leafless trees made the landscape surrounding the school very different from the narrow street of small houses at home. At the end of our street was a smouldering pit-mound; the coal mine and the brick works were close by and we could always smell the bone and glue factory. I was unaccustomed to being in a class with other children. But after the bitter homesickness of the first year I liked it very much there. I still have the friends I made at school. Until their deaths recently I corresponded regularly with my music mistress, known affectionately as the Hag, and with my English mistress, the Bug – also with affection. I think of their teaching with gratitude. I realise too that they can't have been much older than I was.

My sister came to school later. She ran away three times and was brought back from the outskirts of Banbury, eight miles away, by the Bug in her little car. One of the boys, equally unhappy, sent a piece of meat home in a letter to demonstrate the awfulness of the food. The village postmistress brought the envelope, dripping with gravy, back to school where it was displayed at Morning Meeting. The whole school had to send their sweet allowance to a charitable institution that week. The postmistress also took responsibility for a telegram I tried to send to my father on his fiftieth birthday – but more of this later.

The village was said to be the coldest place, next to Aldershot, in England. It was a point of honour never to wear overcoats except on Sundays to Meeting. (Consequently many of us were obliged to go on wearing school overcoats for many years till they wore out.) There were three springs in the village, water bubbled and flowed cold and clear over pebbles at the side of the street. Villagers fetched their water every day. Later the springs were covered and green-painted hand pumps were placed there. Once during the mobilisation some soldiers camped by the pump immediately outside our school. Though told not to we could not resist going out after dark into the freezing evening to stand by their fire and to exchange stories and trophies with these handsome men in their new uniforms. We took our supper, slices of dry bread, out to them. They accepted the offering with well-mannered gratefulness though it was clear they had plenty of nice things, like baked beans, which we did not have. They wrote, in their best writing, in our autograph books: *It's a grand life if you don't weaken* and *Fight the good fight but don't fight too hard.* One of them gave me a button off his coat which I still have. I had no idea then, in spite of the ideals of pacifism, just what pain and mutilation I was to witness in the course of my work not much later on. These men were on their way then to what was to follow as a result of the War.

Because of the strong pacifist attitude, which I shared and still do share, in the school, those of us who had defied authority were subjected to the All Day punishment the next day, supervised by the music mistress, the Hag. The routine began at 7 a.m. with an icy strip wash. Our free time before lunch and before tea, usually given to roller skating, was occupied by two more of these freezing washings. Pent up hilarity was in evidence along the row of unprivate wash basins. We were not allowed to speak. Being *on silence* all day was the chief form of punishment at the school. We developed the ability to use the 'deaf and dumb' alphabet with an efficiency which proved useful in my work later. Other punishments for both boys and girls were cleaning windows with wet newspapers, digging weeds out of the tennis courts, and helping the headmaster's wife to make marmalade.

Because it was a small school there was always the chance to be in the school play even if you could not learn by heart or act. And to get into the First Eleven hockey team was not impossible. We played matches at country schools and against village ladies. Once, in order to avoid showing gaps, we sewed our brown woollen stockings to our knickers. As we ran about the field the result was disastrous.

There is not space to elaborate on my Golden Greetings telegram to my father. The postmistress hovered with her freshly sharpened pencil and crossed out all my best words – congratulations, venerable, half a century, jubilee, beloved – reducing the message to *Loving birthday wishes* followed by my name. My first editor? Perhaps.

I still have my *Golden Treasury of the Bible*, two grey nondescript books, Part I a fat book of the Old Testament and Part II, slim, the New Testament. There is a pencil drawing of Shirley Temple, or rather her ringlets, in the back of Part I. Part II has pages 'The Good Samaritan' and 'The Prodigal Son' marked for one of my children in 1950 so I must have looked at it *fairly* recently . . .

Until now I had forgotten completely Shirley Temple's curls.

CHARLES CAUSLEY
After School

I left school a month before my sixteenth birthday in August 1933. My mother, apprehensive of the currently huge unemployment figures, had arranged for me to work as a clerk in the office of a local builder. I was a docile boy and it didn't occur to me to object, but the news was a considerable shock. I had sat for the Oxford School Certificate examinations earlier in the summer, but results were not expected for some weeks. I had no notion of what sort of career I might follow, nor was it ever discussed at the grammar school. This was long before the days of the Parent-Teacher Association, and working-class parents, in particular, were chary of approaching school authorities for any reason whatever. Schoolteachers, especially grammar-school teachers, were icons of authority and best kept at a distance from home. At all events, after a token fortnight's holiday (I had been looking forward to six weeks) I found myself working for the Tamar Valley Building Company, managing director Mr Leo Finn.

Mr Finn's father, a fierce and indomitable old gentleman, had originally founded the business. His insistence on the highest standards was legendary. If he considered the building of a wall substandard, he thought nothing of demolishing it personally with a sledge hammer and demanding that the quavering workman should start again. By the time I joined the firm old Mr Finn had died and the business had passed to young Leo, an altogether more easy-going figure of great amiability who had served in France in the First World War and had had the misfortune to step on a mine and lose a foot. ('Blown six feet in the air, I was, Charlie. What do you think o' that?') This was the only reference he ever made to me of the War or his injury. He scorned the use of a walking stick and limped swiftly and resolutely about the various building sites with what seemed to me to be incredible energy.

The Tamar Valley Building Company didn't have what I regarded as a proper, purpose-built office at all. It was, in fact, a small converted greenhouse stuck in a corner at the side of Leo's house. Here, the most imposing article of furniture was a large roll-top desk with a heavy chair of equally imposing proportions. For the rest, there were two long wooden tables, shelves crammed with box-files and catalogues from builders' merchants, architects' specifications for various building jobs, as well as rows of boxes containing small items of ironmongery because it was thought unwise to leave them unattended in the general workshop a hundred yards up the road.

My companion was Harry Field, an extremely short-sighted architect, also secretary and director of the company. Like Leo, he was a kindly man (he must have known I was a square peg in a round hole) and always treated me with great consideration. He also had his First World War story, in his case the scene of his rejection from military service. ('Read the letters on that card.' 'What card?' 'On the door.' 'What door?') Both men were permanent smokers, Harry of pipe, Leo of cigarettes. Leo also relieved his feelings by driving a succession of cars – always a Riley – very skilfully and very fast; Harry by practising the organ (inevitably Bach) in the gallery of the local Baptist Chapel.

The other occupant of the office was Leo's bulldog, Brazen, on a blanket in the knee-hole of Leo's desk. Brazen, a savage-looking creature of surprisingly sweet disposition, was devoted to Leo and followed him everywhere, even if he merely rose from his chair and took two steps to answer the telephone. Owing to the brisk pace at which Leo walked, Brazen, seriously overweight, was in a state of permanent exhaustion. He fell asleep easily, and office conferences were often punctuated by his snores and thunderous farts.

My duties were simple. I answered the phone, helped Harry with estimates, dealt with the wages, typed letters and accounts with two fingers. Leo was rarely in the office; Harry often out surveying. The work was undemanding, cosy, lonely and excruciatingly boring.

The workforce, for a small Cornish market town, was quite large: varying between sixty and eighty. Nobody (quite common in the district) was a member of a trades union. The men worked a forty-four-hour week and the rates ranged from 10d. (labourers) to 1/3d. (craftsmen) an hour. The labourers, after deductions for health and unemployment insurance, took home £1.15.1d. a week. My own wage was 12/6d. In the face of fierce competition for jobs, Leo told me that on occasion unemployed men had offered to work for less pay. I asked him if he had ever taken any on. He grinned. 'No.'

I worked in the office for four years. At first I had the vague notion that someone from my school would turn up and explain to my mother that grants or scholarships might provide opportunities for further education for those such as myself who had found it necessary to get employment, however badly paid, in order to contribute to the domestic budget. I also believed that the act of leaving school was irrevocable; that it would be impossible, anyhow, to return. One morning, later in that first August, Leo appeared in the doorway with *The Western Morning News*. 'School Certificate results, boy,' he said. 'You got five credits.' But even with this modest imprimatur, I knew that I was doomed.

It gradually dawned on me that if anyone was going to help me it was I. My secret, unspoken ambition ever since I was a small child was to become a writer: a real writer, who wrote books. The aim was unspoken because I knew it would be received with incredulity, incomprehension. In my family, farm workers, hedgers, ditchers and dry-stone wallers, grooms, gardeners, painters and decorators, quarrymen and railwaymen were the norm. Always rather feeble physically and bereft of any manual skill, I am certain the general feeling about me was probably that I'd got rather a good number by becoming a clerk. And people with my sort of background didn't write books.

My mother was a First World War widow. I was an only child, solitary, a very early reader. Always I had sampled, if not gobbled up entirely, every printed passage I came across. It was at the age of sixteen that I discovered, through a friend, the existence of *The New Statesman & Nation*, then priced sixpence. Originally, I read it not for its socialist political content but for its arts pages, which included poetry, at the back of the paper.

My friend Hector Jory, five years my senior and the statutory small-town communist and revolutionary, was an unemployed linotype operator who had a room in one of the poorest quarters of the town. He was deathly pale with a high, bushy black head of hair and (very daring) affected red ties and pullovers. He skimped on food and drink and spent every spare penny on books. His room was lined with left-wing publications and pamphlets, odd copies of *The Daily Worker*, editions of H.G. Wells, Bertrand Russell, Bernard Shaw. With the founding of Victor Gollancz's Left Book Club his library increased (as did mine) with the addition of such eye-opening works as W.F.R. Macartney's prison autobiography *Walls Have Mouths* and Orwell's *The Road to Wigan Pier*. I was also certain that Hector was discriminated against in the matter of employment because of his political opinions, though he never spoke of this.

Meanwhile, off our particular stage, Hitler's Germany ground steadily into action. It would have required a brain of stone for any member of my generation to live through the teenage years without the inner certainty that a European war was inevitable. For me, the dark intimations of Auden's famous poem of 1932 were warning and prophecy enough.

O what are they doing with all that gear;
What are they doing this morning, this morning?
Only the usual manoeuvres, dear,
Or perhaps a warning.

I was already enthralled by the writings of Auden, Spender, Day-Lewis, Isherwood and others whose work I had come across in John Lehmann's *New Writing* and *New Writing and Daylight*, and by the fact that Lehmann recruited new and exciting writers from all over the globe and printed what they had to say.

One evening I went to a drama festival in Plymouth and saw my first Ibsen: the opening scenes of *A Doll's House*. It was a revelation and led me on to Strindberg and, later, Brecht. I began, without much confidence, to experiment with the writing of poems and plays myself. Despite my earnest reading, I hadn't learned that the surest subjects of creative art reside under one's nose. The people and events of my little Cornish home town seemed to me too drab, too parochial, too uninteresting to qualify as subject matter.

Yet life, outside the office, was lively enough. At one point, slightly to my alarm, I was invited to play the piano for an amateur concert party that toured local village halls throughout the winter raising money for various charities. I was, and still am, an appallingly bad sight-reader, but given time found I could manage some sort of accompaniment. My greatest successes were in playing for the comedian and the comedienne; both were brilliant performers but neither of them could read a note of music. They were liable to ad lib, start and finish, as and when the fancy took them. This always appealed to me and I discovered that I was a dab hand at extemporisation. The straight singers, however, were less enthusiastic about my tendency to add fancy bits to what I considered to be rather tame and uninteresting printed accompaniments. The hard-working baritone ('Sea Fever', 'Glorious Devon', 'The Sergeant-Major's on Parade') refused finally to allow me to play for him at all and the soprano ('A Spring Morning', 'Vilia', 'My Curly-Headed Babby'), also a pianist, was drafted in.

A slightly more attractive option presented itself when the bank-clerk

181

pianist in a four-piece dance band, The Rhythm Boys, was suddenly transferred to another branch, and I was offered the job. Pay was in cash at the end of each gig. By this time my weekly office salary had risen to 15s. For a night with the band the reward was a flat 10s. for four hours, sometimes higher in the case of classier engagements such as Masonics or Golf Club dinners and dances.

It was tough on the fingers, but the money was more than acceptable and I went halves with my mother to help out with the housekeeping. We were a motley-looking outfit. The drummer, also the business manager, was a thin, pale and determined hairdresser. The clarinettist and the violinist were both ex-military bandsmen who contrived always to sit at attention and play absolutely everything quite tirelessly and with deadly accuracy, each with one eye strictly on the clock. The fourth member, a saxophonist, was also the clown of the outfit, guaranteed to raise the spirits during the last awful hour of an engagement. His main concern was to get home in time for an hour or two's sleep before rising to deliver the mail.

My chief memory of those nights is of the almost uniformly dreadful pianos: battered and sullen relics, rich in broken and rusted strings, missing keys, snapped pedals and cigarette burns. They were sometimes complete with fretwork fronts, tattered silk, brass candlesticks with lighted candles which, a serious fire-risk, usually fell off early on in the proceedings.

It now seems to me extraordinary how little most of us knew, all the same, of the surrounding countryside. Neither I nor any of my contemporaries could afford a car, let alone a motor bike. But the formation of a hiking club changed the situation. Once a week, in the summer months, to the jeers of those who accused us of not walking anywhere but of simply going for a ride, we'd set off from the town square in a hired bus. Our objective was a base point from which we could walk a few miles to an ancient hill fort, a holy well, an Elizabethan farmhouse, a ruined canalway: always ending at a pub from which we were collected in the bus. For myself, my forays into the surrounding district with the concert party and the band were almost always in the winter and in the dark. It was a pleasant change to see what places looked like by day.

Our most memorable hiking trip, unquestionably, was when we decided to navigate the great granite sea of Bodmin Moor to Cornwall's highest point, Brown Willy. Midsummer Eve was approaching and, an ancient custom, a chain of bonfires was to be lit through the county from

Penzance in the west to Kit Hill in the east. Off we went, on the Eve of St John. Every detail was planned, including a session of folk dancing on the summit accompanied by the town band in their lion-tamers' uniforms. It was a beautiful, clear evening as we set off in the bus, speeding to loud cheers past the cycling club off on some other unspecified Midsummer Eve jaunt.

We arrived at the moorland village of Altarnun, apparently to collect our guide. This was the first I had heard of a guide – a sinister and solemn word in my vocabulary. From Altarnun, Brown Willy looked as though it was about four miles away over the stone Cornish hedge and across the open moor. Nobody but a fool, I thought, could miss it. All that was required was to walk straight ahead.

Voicing this, I was soon put in place by my more experienced companions. Distances, they said, were deceptive on the moor. Night was falling, the sky clouding. There was every likelihood of mist, even fog; the certainty of bogs. The journey had also to be made back over the moor by another route after dark for a pasty supper in the Jamaica Inn at Bolventor.

I was unimpressed, at first, by the guide: not, as I'd expected, a gnarled veteran of the moor but a schoolboy dressed up in a cowboy outfit. 'He knaw'th the moor like the back of 'e's 'and, that boy,' I heard somebody say. I almost decided to stay in the bus, but fearing the contempt of my companions I simply vowed not to let that boy out of my sight until we got back to Jamaica: nor did I.

Everything, or almost everything, happened as the gloomy prophets had predicted. The bogs glittered unpleasantly. The mists rose and rain fell as we plodded up the one thousand, three hundred and seventy-five feet of Brown Willy, where the rain came on harder and heavier and the mists thicker and quicker. The town band formed up and started valiantly on 'Sellinger's Round' and 'Gathering Peascods' and the dancers stumbled about on the springy turf in the increasing blackness. After tremendous efforts, the bonfire was forced into life and we were able, finally, like a troop of broody Druids, to begin the trek back to Jamaica. The weather grew worse. One dancer had plunged a foot down a rabbit hole and twisted her ankle and, alternately groaning lightly and apologising loudly, was carried in an improvised hammock by four of our group. All eyes strained ahead for the guide, with his lantern. The band, strung out in a straggling line well to the rear, kept in touch with one another by sounding off their instruments: a honk from a trombone here, a bray from a euphonium there, a startled answer from some of the lively black moorland cattle everywhere around us.

In the general confusion, an important folk-rite had been forgotten. Nobody had remained on the summit to gather some ashes from the last of the sacred fire: ashes as a charm against the evil eye, against sterility, crop failure, murrain in cattle. When at last we arrived at Jamaica we all somehow seemed unsurprised to be greeted with the news that the pasties had all gone: eaten by the cycling club.

Settling myself in the bus for the homeward journey, I noticed Wally Penhale, a schoolfriend and devoted fan of The Rhythm Boys, making his way towards the empty seat beside me. Wally's father was manager of the Gas, Light & Coke Company. Gazing around conspiratorially, Wally lowered his voice. 'Hey,' he said. 'Dad says your firm's looking a bit rocky. He says would you like to go and see him. Might have a job for you. Sounds all right.'

I thanked him; said I would. For the remainder of the trip I remember we talked of the dreadful counterpoint to our local activities on the world scene: of the Italian occupation of Abyssinia and the use of poison gas, the Spanish Civil War in full bloody swing and the radio bulletins filled with accounts of the bombing of cities and civilians, British Movietone News with its spectacles of Nazi tens of thousands rallying at Nuremberg. 'Wally,' I said. 'What do you think of Hitler? What do you make of it?' 'Looks like we're for it,' said Wally. He sounded quite cheerful.

HONE TUWHARE

Irises

(for Joan de Arc & Vincent)

Van Gogh's spiritual sister Joan dropped by today fisting a peanut butter
    jar full of tremulous irises. The irises were velvet-soft and purply; the
    fragile blooms showing off their centres which flared like peacock
    tailfeathers or Hawaiian beach-shirts billowing on a clothesline. But
    some were in bud, closed down and private, like moths' wings on their
    day off.

In a warm room like this, said the Maid of Orleans, they'll open out – all
    of them. Have you got some water?

I turned the tap on and Joan filled the jar nearly to the top. I took it away
    from her and placed the irises on top of the radio where they trembled
    to the beat of music.

Vincent thought you might like some fresh irises today, so I picked some
    from a garden – full of them – that he was trying to paint.
    Hey, I'm not complaining, I said. Nature is art's finest lover; its best –
    and ONLY student. They're . . . exquisite, I said, already in debit.
    Beauty doesn't make a thing of it, she said, they're just so . . .
    momently. I'd like a drink of water –

I can do better than that, I said, producing a glass into which I poured
    some dry red wine from a green bottle, and pressed from grapes off
    vines from Dalmatia growing on dairy flats at Kumeu. I topped it up
    with cubistic water from the fridge discantating all the while like a fussy
    guru – to take my mind off Joan's suit of rough red cloth which I hoped
    would not suddenly go up in flames, just now.

For Joan wasn't wearing her white armour made in Tours, a city famous
    for its armourers, or sword with five crosses on it and banner, on which
    was painted her own motto: JESUS MARIA.

Joan did not ride up on a fierce horse with cross eyes, muscles bunched, nostrils flaring. Instead, she came on a four-wheeled charger which purred when you turned the motor on. I don't know how she got away with it going through the lights at 130 km, with the irises lolling around in the plastic jar on the seat beside her. A special messenger from the rainbow goddess, Aniwa-niwa? Hell, I'm in love with the world again.

Merci: and kia ora, I said, handing her the glass of wine and water. In one go, I downed mine. But Joan rolled the first mouthful around for a while, before swallowing: Mon Dieu! she breathed, I can smell the wine, you, me, the irises – everything! Salut.

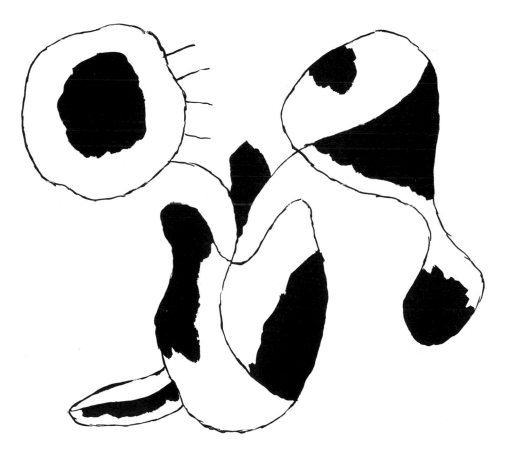

HELEN GARNER
A Vigil

'Every angel is terrible.'
– R. M. Rilke

Kim's father was supposed to come down from Queensland, or wherever he lived, to straighten her life out for her, give her some good advice, pay her uni fees and so on, or even take her back up there to live with him. He promised he'd be there in June, for her birthday, but for some reason he couldn't make it by the date. Then it was going to be August, then September. She was hanging out for this. She stopped going anywhere, in case he turned up while she was out and the others in the house let him get away without giving him her message, to make himself at home and wait ten minutes. First she used to sew, till the machine broke down, and anyway the whine of the motor was starting to make her nervous. Then she drew, or wrote for hours in her diary. Then she read, lying on her bed nibbling at the ends of her hair, but she said the books she was supposed to be studying were so boring that she kept dozing off.

Then things got to the point with her where all she could do was sleep. Awake, whatever she heard threw her into a state of nerves: the wind when it bumped, a bird in a tree outside the window, the water rustling down the gutters when the council workers opened the hydrants. Her fearfulness filled Raymond with impatient scorn, and relief that he was not after all the most hopeless person he knew. The morning a truck poured a ton of blue metal chips down in the lane outside, he came back from the kitchen and found her on her knees in the corner with her head in the dirty-clothes bag. He thought of laughing, till he saw that her eyes were bulging. There was a primary school behind where she lived. She couldn't stand the noise the kids made in the yard at playtime, their screaming. It made her grind her teeth and blow her nose till it went red.

'Somebody must be hurting them,' she whispered. 'They're hurting each other.'

'You're stupid,' said Raymond irritably. 'That's a *good* sound. Aren't kids supposed to be a good thing? You shouldn't freak out over something that's *good*. What's the matter with you?'

By October, though she lied about it, she was swallowing day by day in threes and fours the pills she got from her mother and sleeping the time away, buried so flat in the quilt and pillows that when he came in he had to feel around to make sure she was still there.

'Get in,' she mumbled, too doped to open her eyes. 'Let's go to sleep.'

Her skin was loose, like old sacks. She had about as much life in her as a half-deflated dummy, but without complaint she opened her legs, and he kept his face turned away, to avoid her breath. She grunted, that was all, and when he rolled away she made a limp effort to attach herself to his back; but she was a dead weight that could not hang on. Her arms' grip weakened and her torso fell away. The cool air of the room shrank his bare spine. She snuffled, and a light rhythmic click began in the open membranes of her throat. He would have got up straight away except that the tick of her breathing matched itself briefly to his heartbeat, and at the moment of focusing on the leaves outside the glass his mind lost its grip on the edges of the furniture and slithered away into a comforting nest, a sty of warm webs and straw. Then the parrot screeched, in somebody's backyard, and he woke.

He raised himself on one elbow and looked over his shoulder at her. She was only a small girl, with small bones, and her head too he had always thought of as small. Wandering round the city, the day after she had first dragged him home from a party where he was lurking sourly in a doorway, always too old or too awkward, always wearing the wrong clothes, he had found himself fitting words together in the part of his mind that no one knew about: he practised remarking casually, 'She's buttery,' or, 'She's well toothed,' but he never fell into conversation with anyone who looked interested in that way of talking – Alby certainly wasn't – and now her face, like any drugged sleeper's, was as thick, stupid and meaningless as a hunk of rock. He saw that there was nothing special about her; that he was superior to her after all. She was damaged goods. The pills were not to blame. The pills were doing him a favour by reminding him of something he had always known was in her, in any girl that age who would do what she did with him, and you could tell by the moron face they made when they were doing it, all vague and grinning. He imagined, propped there in his twisted pose while his insides congealed again into blankness, how we would describe her in the café if any of them stopped talking long enough: 'She was more out of it than I've ever seen her. Mate, she was' – he would stick out his flat hands, palms down, and jerk them sharply apart – 'out of it. This gig's over. People who can't get their shit together should just go and die.'

It was late in the day. If he got up now he could make it to the Hare Krishnas for a feed. The girl downstairs was getting ready for work. As she called to her cat, her clogs on the cobbles of the lane made a sound like a tennis ball bouncing. While he pulled on his clothes, blocking out the irritating click of Kim's open mouth, he ran his eyes over the floor, checking for dropped coins, a screwed-up five-dollar note, the price of a coffee, anything he could use.

On the boards between the bed and the door stood a pair of heavy black rubber-soled shoes. Their laces were still in bows. She must have yanked them off in her rush back to the big dipper of sleep, and yet they were placed tidily side by side, and although they were months old they still looked new, since the only wear they got was when she walked over to her mother's every couple of days for pills and maybe a leftover from the fridge. All the girls wore these shoes. He felt nothing about the style. He only noticed the shoes because the neat bows jigged a memory which was gone before his mind could lumber round to it: something about laces, something about tying a shoe. He hesitated, then he stepped over the shoes and went out of the room. The door clicked shut behind him. The air of the stairs was thick with the smell of cooking broccoli.

Four days passed before he came back.

He too spent them horizontal, in his brother's boarding-house room with his pants unzipped, holding across his chest Alby's big acoustic guitar and picking at it tunelessly, or rereading the collection of seventies comic books from under the bed: epic acid landscapes, hulking heroes in fur leggings, pinheads, VW buses full of frizzy hair, a stoned cat, girls with huge legs in boots and mini skirts, and a special way of walking called 'truckin''. That world, drawn in square boxes and balloons of words, he knew. The real one he was lost in, but so lost that he didn't know he was lost. His father was dead, his mother was stupid, his sister had run away; and as soon as Alby got back he would be on the street again. He lived untouched inside a grey casing through which he watched, dully, how other people behaved, and sometimes tried to mimic them. He saw that they remarked on the weather, and he tried to remember to look at the sky, to see if there were clouds in it. He saw what people ate, and he bought some. He saw that they talked to make each other laugh, and he dropped his mouth open to make the sound 'Ha. Ha.' He saw that, when a band played, they heard something; he saw that they danced, and he tried to lift his feet. His whole life was faking. He thought that was what people did.

At six o'clock on Tuesday he cleaned himself up and went out. He passed Kim's mother leaving the Lebanese take-away with a felafel roll in each hand

and a heavy-looking bloke coming down the step behind her. 'G'day, Ursula,' he said. She nodded, but the bloke gave him a dirty look and Raymond dropped his eyes. He got himself some chips and ate them as he walked to Kim's, stopping for a look in the window of a second-hand shop that sold things Alby might need: a stringless guitar or a plastic record-rack or books with titles like *Chiropody Today* or *Welcome to Bulbland*. The tattoo shop was open. The artist skulked right down at the back, crouching in a burst chair with wooden arms. No thanks. You could get Aids off those needles, though maybe a little anchor, a bluebird . . .

The small concrete yard of Kim's house was scattered with faded junk mail and plastic pots of grey dirt and stalks. He tossed the chip paper against the fence, wiped his hands on his thighs, and pressed the buzzer. She might ask him if it was 'a nice evening'. That kind of talk she picked up from her mother. He directed his eyes upwards and saw grey: a grey sky, grey air. It was not raining. Was that 'nice'? The clog girl opened. Her boyfriend was in a band and once, when he had gone away on tour without taking her and Kim was staying the night at her mother's, the girl, who Raymond believed fancied him, had blundered into Kim's room bawling, wanting an audience for her sob story. She was disgusting. Raymond lay there on Kim's bed, staring up at the girl. He said, 'Oh, go away. Go away or I'll shoot you. To put you out of your misery.' Now, seeing who he was, she turned away without speaking and headed for the back of the house. From the foot of the stairs, before he started to climb, Raymond glanced after her. He saw her shoulder and heel disappear into the kitchen. The bulb hanging there was lit. It swung slightly, and the shadow above it swung too. This he would remember.

Kim's door was closed. There were no voices, and no light showed under it, so he turned the handle and walked straight in. The room was stuffy, and almost dark. He stepped round the low bed, flicked back the curtain and pushed up the window, wedging it open with a hunk of chair leg she kept on the sill. Better air came in under the raised curtain, and, at the same instant, in the tree right outside the room, a bird started to sing. He could see it, in against the trunk. It was a small bird but a loud one, and it was shrilling and yelling without any tune, making the kind of racket that sent Kim into fits. He felt a surge of meanness. Holding up the curtain with one hand, he turned his head to watch her wake.

The bed was a turned-over confusion of materials. Only the crests of the folds caught the light. Where was her face? Was she even there? This stupid bird! It was louder than a whole treeful of cicadas and still she didn't hear it. There was a pale bit of her up between the pillows but her hair had got darker

193

and was growing in the wrong place. He stood there with one hand tangled in the curtain, feeling for a nail to hook it back. It caught, but still the light on the bed kept darkening: he was straining to make out her face. Outside, the bird shrilled and thrilled. Her hair had turned black and was growing across her chin. He pulled his hand out of the curtain folds and threw himself to his knees on the very edge of the mattress. It bounced. The smell hit him. Her mouth, half open, was clogged with vomit and alive with a busyness of insects. His head and torso jerked back as if on a rein. He made no sound, but across the ridges of his windpipe rushed the shrieking, the squalling, of the bird in the tree behind.

He reeled down the stairs and out on to the street. It was almost night. The rooflines of the houses sliced a green and bitter sky. Bells tinkled in showers and somebody was feebly panting, but otherwise the soundtrack had shut down. He kept walking, bumping the shop windows with his shoulder, dragging the soles of his rubber thongs. He blundered past a man sharpening his fingernails on a red-brick wall, a barefaced waitress swabbing terrace tables, a busker unpacking a saxophone in a doorway. He was heading for Alby's, if Alby's still existed; it must, it must, and he travelled slowly, trying to keep himself unfocused, for if he stayed submerged long enough he might surface at last flat on his back under Alby's scratchy grey blanket and open his eyes to see Kim standing crossly beside the bed, trampling Alby's comics with her heavy shoes, scowling at him and biting the split ends off her hair. But the night went on and on, and he ran out of vagueness. It gave out on him. He came to the end of it, and then he knew that nobody on earth, nobody he would ever hear of or meet, had the authority to rescue him from the cold fact of what had happened; and yet, as he slunk along the avenue where the mercury vapour lights flushed and whitened, he gazed with stupid longing at the line of spruikers outside the porn clubs, kings of the pavement, big fast-talking, dangerous boys in long black overcoats and greasy little ponytails who moved him to awe as angels would, they were so tall, so graceful, so inky with unused power.

He was shoving his spare shirt into a bag when the knock came at Alby's front door. What day was it? Sun was shining. It felt like afternoon. He opened the door and Ursula was standing there. He looked quickly behind her for blokes, but she was on her own. Her face under the sunglasses was fatter, and she was dressed in black.

'Get in the car,' said Ursula.

A taxi was waiting at the kerb, with the door open and the motor running. He hung back.

'Do up your fucking shirt and get in the car,' she said. Her voice was hoarse and she smelt of grog, not beer, something stronger and sweeter. His legs weakened. He had not spoken for two days and he could not speak now. He followed her to the cab. As she climbed in ahead of him, he saw the gold chain round her ankle.

This was one of the few taxi rides of Raymond's life and he was worried that the driver, an Asian in a clean white shirt, would think he was a bludger or up himself for taking a cab at all instead of public transport, and also that he might think he had something to do with this puffy, purple-faced moll who tore in cigarette smoke with all her back teeth showing and kept letting out panting noises and wiping under her sunglasses with the bottom of her dress. She had a flagon of sherry in a plastic bag between her feet and every few minutes she bent over, tipped it sideways, and took a swallow. Raymond sat with his hands clasped between his tightly clenched thighs, and kept his eyes on the shiny head-rest in front of his face.

The place, when at last the taxi swerved off the freeway and followed the signs to its gates, looked more like a golf course than a cemetery. It was vast, bare and trim. At the end of its curved black road they came to a garden, and in it, a building. Ursula shoved him out, pushing the wrapped flagon into his hands, and he stood there sweating while she paid the driver and the taxi drove away. At the mouth of the chapel some people in a group turned towards them and stared. Raymond thought they were looking at him, but it was Ursula they were watching out for, they were waiting for Ursula to arrive. They must be her friends from before; they were old hippies with grey curls or beards, and the women had hair that was long and stiff, or else cut short like boys', showing their wrinkled eyes and foreheads. One of the men was tall and bony, like a skeleton, with a shaved head and rotten teeth; his hands were tattooed. Ursula kept a tight grip on Raymond's elbow. To the people staring it might have seemed that she was using his arm for support but in fact he was her prisoner, she was yanking him along beside her in a shuffle, in at the chapel door, through a cluster of whispering girls with massed hair and black bodies, and right up the aisle to the empty seats in the front row.

Yellow light fell from long windows at the sides. More people, not many, were waiting in the seats and someone was playing one of those organs that quiver automatically. Ursula was different now. She was trying to act normal. Raymond heard her put on a voice and say to the woman on her other side,

'What a lot of people have turned up!' The woman tried to put her arm round Ursula's waist, but Ursula went stiff, and the woman, with an offended look, took her arm away and moved across the aisle to a seat further back. Raymond sneaked the flagon under the seat and pushed it out of sight with his foot. As he straightened up someone tapped him sharply on the shoulder. He jerked round. A woman in the seat behind, with wrinkles on her top lip as if from whistling, leaned forward and spoke to him in a furtive way.

'What? What?' he said in confusion.

'I said you were Kimmy's boyfriend, weren't you?' said the woman. She slid her eyes over his face, ears, hair, neck.

'No, no,' he jabbered. 'Not me, no, it wasn't me. Friend of the family, I'm a friend. Of the family.'

His head was shaking itself like a puppet's. He turned his back on her and hunched his shoulders up round his ears. In the front row there was no protection. He could not fold or bend his legs enough; his feet were enlarged, gross, dirty.

The music stopped and a man in a suit stepped uncertainly up to the front and stood against some curtains, facing the people. Raymond did not know whether they were supposed to stand or sit. He glanced behind him for a clue. A couple of the girls were scrambling to their feet, one bloke dropped on to his knees, but most of the people stayed seated with stiff, embarrassed faces. The man out the front said nothing, gave no orders. He did not appear to be in charge: no one was in charge. Raymond realised that nobody here knew how this thing was meant to be done, that nobody here was going to stand up and say the words that would save them.

Then he heard, in the uncomfortable hush, a squeaking and a gliding, the sound of small wheels. Ursula's nails sank into his arm. The curtains at the front were nosed apart and, into the empty space where the weak man in the suit was waiting, rolled, on a metal trolley, the wooden box with Kim inside it.

Ursula stood up, dragging him with her. Her fingers bit into his inner elbow; and now out of her mouth horrible sounds began, ugly and ridiculous, the noises that bad singers make when they work up to a solo: 'Woh, woh, woh,' she went, blank and gaping, gobbling for breath. An old woman darted across and seized her shoulders with both hands but Ursula flung up one arm and knocked her away. In the same movement she struck off her own sunglasses which dangled from one ear and hung half across her mouth, revealing two swollen bruises: her eyes. Out of these sore slits poured a gaze that hit the end of the coffin and bored right in. Ursula at that moment could see through wood.

196

She turned on Raymond with a crazy mouth. He fought to break away, but like the shrilling of the bird outside the window Ursula's howling, this horror, exploded and stuffed the universe, paralysed him, swallowed him whole.

Then the bald skeleton with tattooed hands stepped right through the commotion in his heavy boots and put both arms round Ursula from behind.

'Let go,' he said, right in her ear, working at her hands, rubbing at them, getting his thumbs under their grip. 'Urs, it's me, Phil. Come on, Urs. It won't help the little girl now. Lay off the poor bastard, Ursula. Come on, let him go.'

He unhooked her claws and Raymond stumbled back on collapsing muscles. A rush of murmuring women with handkerchiefs and skirts flowed into the space where he had been, but in the second before they engulfed her he saw her one last time, with her back against the bald man's chest, rearing, her arms pinned up by his grip on her two wrists: her face was a demon's muzzle, sucking in air before its final plunge into the chasm.

Raymond got to his feet in the corner where he had been flung. The air in the ugly chapel settled; the coffin hummed behind him. He could not look at it, but he felt it vibrating in the yellow air, rippling out waves that pressed against his back and propelled him, on chalky stumps whose height continually changed, down the aisle towards the door. Ankle-deep in crushed garlands he crossed the porch and stopped on the step of the building, swaying and hanging on to the sides of the archway. He slid his head out into the garden. The last of the cars was pulling away. He heard the sponge and pop of its tyres on the bitumen, saw the blurred hair-masses of the girls packed into the back seat, smelled the exhaust that shot out of its low muffler. It swung round the curve in the road, and was gone.

He let his knees buckle, and sat down hard on the step. He was empty. There was nothing left inside him at all. He crouched there on the chapel's lip, rolling up his shirtsleeve to inspect the site of his bruises. If he could work out where he was, if he could find his way to the gate, he was free to get out of here, to drag himself away.

So when the heavy boots came crunching towards him across the car-park, although the skin of his skull tightened and a thousand hairs grew stiff, he did not raise his head. Maybe it was the gardener. Maybe it was the first person arriving for the next funeral. He kept very still. He made himself narrow. He waited, with shoulders clenched, for the boots to pass.

They halted in front of him. In his stupor and weakness, Raymond fixed his eyes on them. Never in his life had he really examined or considered the meaning of what anyone wore on their feet. The boots were very worn. They were black, and old. They met the ground with leisurely authority, and yet their cuban heels gave them a lightness, a fanciful quality that was poised, vain, almost feminine. The man whose boots they were, from whose footwear Raymond was trying to read his fate, breathed steadily in and out. He was in no hurry. Still Raymond did not raise his eyes.

At last the grating voice began. 'So you were the one, were you?' it said. 'You were the one who was fucking her.'

Raymond made blinkers round his face with his cupped hands and kept his eyes on the boots. 'No, mate,' he said. 'Not me.' He hardly recognised the sound of himself, his usual dismal babble of lies. 'Oh, I knew her, sure. Sure thing. I knew Kim. Everyone knew Kim. She was a nice girl. But I only came today because Ursula, because her mother wanted me to.'

The boots shifted, emitting a faint leathery squeak. 'Bit old for her, weren't you?'

A whiff of cigarette smoke dropped to Raymond's level and spiked the lining of his nose. 'Listen, mate,' he said, cupping his eyes, keeping his eyes down, 'you've got the wrong bloke. It wasn't me. I don't know who she –'

'Anyway,' said the man, moving his weight on to his left foot. 'She's dead now. No point worrying who was up who. Is there?'

'This is right,' said Raymond. 'Nothing can help her now.'

Over in the garden beyond the car-park a bird uttered three notes of a mounting song, and fell silent.

A butt landed with force on the black ground beside the boots. It lay on its side, saliva-stained, twisted, still burning; Raymond could not resist, at last, the urge to reach out one foot and perform the little circular dance of crushing it. Still he did not look up.

'There is one thing, though,' said the low, harsh voice above him. 'There's one more thing that has to be done. For the girl.'

'I have to go, actually,' said Raymond. He drew in his feet and placed his hands on the step as if to stand. This movement raised his gaze to the knees of the man's black jeans: the cloth was beaten, necessary, seldom washed, carelessly pulled on: as flexible as skin. 'I think I'll get on home,' said Raymond. 'I have to find my brother.'

'Hang on,' said the voice, patiently, firmly. 'You can't leave yet. I want to show you something.'

The boots took two steps back, then another two, then two more. The garden, until now blotted out by the hugeness of the boots, the legs, the voice, spread suddenly into Raymond's frame of vision. This he did not want. He did not want movement, noise, softness; he wanted a permanent berth inside his grey casing.

He raised his chin to argue.

Where one man had been standing, there now were two. Raymond sat in his crouched posture, head back, on the threshold of the chapel. His lips parted to speak, but he could not properly see the two men's faces, for the afternoon sun hung exactly behind their two heads which were leaning together ear to ear, calmly regarding him, waiting calmly for his next burst of excuses; and these died in his mouth at the sight of the corona of light whose centre was their pair of skulls, one furred with yellow hair, one shaven bald as ivory.

The two men stepped apart.

'I know who you are,' said Raymond to the bald man. Again his own voice rang oddly to him, as if his thoughts were forming on his tongue and not in his brain. 'Are you her father?'

'Hardly,' said the bald man, and laughed. 'Don't be a dickhead *all* your life.'

The men looked at each other, swung their heads to take in the moving garden, then fixed their eyes again on Raymond. They're crims, thought Raymond. They've been in the nick. The one with hair was dressed in ironed grey trousers and a maroon blazer with gold on the pocket. He must have a job at a racecourse or out the front of a tourist hotel. He wore boots as well but cheap brown ones, hard-looking, though polished. He glanced at his watch. His hands too were tattooed, with bitten nails.

'Come on, Phil,' he said to the bald man. 'The next mob will be on my back at four.'

The bald man, catching Raymond's eye, clicked his tongue and jerked his head sideways. 'Hop up, pal,' he said. 'We want to show you something.'

Raymond got to his feet warily, brushing the seat of his pants.

'Tsk,' said the man in the blazer, to himself. 'People don't care *what* they wear to a funeral these days.'

He took a toothpick out of his blazer pocket, jammed it between his back teeth, and clomped away along a narrow path that skirted the chapel's outer wall. The bald man pushed Raymond lightly between the shoulder blades, and himself trod close behind. A freckled man in a towelling hat passed them and went tramping away across an enormous lawn, wheeling a barrow and whistling with raised eyebrows and cheerful trills. All three men greeted each other in an old-fashioned way, with grimaces and clicks.

Raymond's legs were still hollow and shaky; but as the men marched him Indian-style along the pathway, not speaking, moving forward with apparent purpose, he began to relax. Maybe this wouldn't be too bad. These men, like uncles, had taken him in hand. He turned to glance at the bald one, who winked at him and nodded. It was a public place, after all. What could go wrong? Maybe he could drop his guard and walk like this between them, single file. It was not so dangerous. He could slide from one thing to the next, and the next; nothing much would be expected of him, the rest of the day would roll by as even the longest of days do, and by the end of it he would have got a lift somewhere, would have walked somewhere, would find himself somewhere, under somebody's roof, maybe with people, maybe on his own; yes, all this he could handle. The worst was over. He turned again to the bald man, and almost smiled at him.

The man in the blazer veered off the path and plunged into the dense strip of hedge that separated it from the building's side. Between two bouncing bushes of blue flowers he rustled his way, spitting out his toothpick, and with key outstretched unlocked a little wooden door marked PRIVATE. He held the springy green branches apart for them with turning thrusts of his shoulders; they joined him, pinned against the wall by whippy shrubbery; he went ahead, and one by one they stooped and stepped through the little door, on to a narrow staircase that led them into the underworld.

The shock of it.

Raymond propped on the stair with one leg in mid-air. Above him the door slammed. The bald man coming close on his heels down the ladder would have cannoned into him, but took the strain with his thighs, and Raymond felt, instead of the weight of a heavy body landing against him, merely a dexterous, light brushing. He lurched down the last step.

Here they had not heard of blood or colour. It was a land made of dust, of chalk, of flour. The walls and floor and ceiling were grey, the air was grey, and, as his gaze cleared and crept deeper, he saw that the receding alley of huge ovens was grey, that the workers who moved silently away between them were grey. The only sound was a low, steady roaring.

'Like it?' said the man in the blazer. 'This is where we work.'

'He runs the place,' said the bald man. 'He's the one who gives the orders.'

The man in the blazer, flattered, gave a naughty shrug. His hand closed round Raymond's aching upper arm, but gently, and urged him forward step by step until he stood, trembling and dumb, bracketed by the two men, in front of the closed door of the first furnace.

'Where is she?' said the bald man. 'He won't want to be kept hanging about.'

'Look up there,' said the man in the blazer, and pointed. 'She's next in line.'

'Ah,' said the bald man in his grating voice, with satisfaction. 'Ah, yes.'

A slot opened high in the grey cement wall, thirty yards away, and out of it, strapped to an elevated conveyor belt, flew the coffin. It dashed down and round the tilted track, skimming fast and cornering suavely on its slender arrangement of rails.

'Yep, here she comes,' said the man in the blazer, giving Raymond's elbow a little squeeze. 'Here comes your girl.'

A single pink posy was still clinging, by an accidental twist of sticky-tape, to the coffin's lid. As the box slid smartly into the last turn of the track and came to a stop beside them at the furnace door, the flowers lost their purchase and sailed in a brief, low arc to the floor. The man in the blazer bobbed down for the bunch. He took a sniff and tossed it over his shoulder into a barrow, while with his other hand, in a smooth movement, he checked a number on the coffin's end and made a mark on a list behind him. He raised his arm in a signal.

The oven door opened.

First, a square of colour: a blossoming, the relief of orange flames. Then a colossal blast of heat which evaporated the moisture off Raymond's eyeballs. He staggered, and the bald man caught him by the arm.

'Steady on,' he said. 'You'll be right.'

Behind them the man in the blazer was deftly unbuckling the straps that had secured the coffin to its sled.

'Here,' he said to Raymond. 'Take an end.'

Raymond's mind had abandoned his body. He obeyed. He turned front-on to the coffin and reached out both arms, but the man in the blazer winked at him and wagged one finger, tick-tock, right in his face.

'Uh-uh,' he said. 'Bad posture. Bend those knees, mate, or you'll fuck your back.'

Raymond bent them. His muscles quivered. He slid his fingers under the narrow end of the coffin and got a grip. The bald man played no part in the operation, but stood close by, watching, with his arms folded mildly over his chest. The man in the blazer took hold of the broad end, and nodded to Raymond. They straightened their legs. So light! The box floated up to waist-level.

'Little scrap of a thing, was she?' said the man in the blazer. 'Weighs no more than a feather.'

The coffin hovered slantwise across the open pop-hole in the furnace door.

The heat was tremendous: their eyes squinted, their heads involuntarily turned away, their tongues dried in their mouths.

'Back up,' said the man in the blazer. 'We'll slip her in head first.'

Raymond shuffled backwards and to one side. The man in the blazer screwed up his face against the blast and flexed his legs just enough to give him leverage. Then, in a series of manoeuvres so rapid, dainty and accurate that in three seconds it was done, he flipped his end of the load on to the lip of the furnace slot, darted back and, nudging Raymond out of the way with his hip, shot the coffin straight through the door and on to the shelf of flame. The door clanged shut. The heat faded. The man took a folded hanky out of his blazer sleeve and mopped his neck.

'A bloke,' he said, 'would be a mug to wear a tie in this line of work.'

Something hard pressed against the backs of Raymond's knees, which gave. It was a chair. The two men stood one on either side of him, each with a hand resting lightly on his shoulder. Like a monarch between courtiers, he sat facing the grey door of the grey oven. When he began to sag, to faint, they held him gently upright, keeping his spine against the chair-back. The wrist-watch of the man on his right ran madly in his ear.

'Sorry about the delay,' said the man in the blazer. 'We have to squirt a bit of oil on to the head and torso, to get them going. But the feet only take a few minutes.'

'The feet?' whispered Raymond. His teeth, his lips were dry: they rubbed against each other wrongly, snagging and missing.

The bald man, whose shaven skull had flushed a delicate pink, looked down at Raymond with sudden interest.

'You want to see?' he said. 'Open up that door.'

They raised Raymond from the chair and half-pressed, half-carried him forward to the furnace. The other man waved, and the door clanked open. Raymond's cheeks clenched of their own accord, turning his eyes to slits. The heat inside the cavern was so intense that all he could see was a working and a wavering. The men supported him tenderly, pointing him towards the square of liquid orange.

'I can't –' he said. 'I can't –'

'Yes, you can,' said the bald man urgently. 'Look now.'

Something in there was wrinkling. The small end of the coffin, fragile as an eggshell, was crinkling into a network of tiny cracks. While Raymond stared, greedy in his swoon of shock, the panel collapsed; it gave way to the swarming orange argument, and where it had been he saw a dark-cored nimbus of flame, seething, closer to him than an arm's reach. Its twin centres, their shod soles towards him, were her feet. In the passion of their transfiguration they loosened. They opened. They fell apart.

He could manage only his neck. The rest he let the two men deal with, and their tattooed hands went on holding him together. The long tube of the coffin now lost form. Pouf! It fell softly in upon itself, her last shelter gone. Deep in the toiling fire he made out a humped, curved lump, and beyond that, rising, a denser clod, her head. He opened his mouth to cry out, but the wetness needed for speech was sucked off the surface of him by the oven's impersonal breath.

The furnace door slammed. He tottered like a doll. They lifted him backwards and placed him on the chair. While his seared skin loosened and turned salty, he hung by the shoulders from the men's restraining hands. He drooped there, sightless, beside himself, his own hallucination. Was there music? Someone was whistling, stacking the notes in jagged steps and executing a long and detailed flourish: a knot cleverly tied, Kim's shoe, the brass eyelets in a double row, the impossible twirl of her fast fingers lacing; a man's voice grew in song, then the fires roared uninterrupted, while near his ear the watch chattered, a tiny hysteria headlong, never arriving, never drawing breath.

'And again,' said the voice.

He half-raised his head, a dog ready for its next beating, and they bore him forward.

The grey door was open. Raymond looked in. The fire and the heat were barely a shimmer in the cavernous air. There was no colour anywhere, except for the maroon blazer-cuff in the outermost corner of Raymond's view. The furnace floor was covered with ordinary ash, and on this desert bed lay scattered in a free arrangement three or four long bones, pale, dry-looking, innocent.

'There,' said the man in the blazer. 'All finished now. You can go home.'

They turned him and unhanded him and dropped him on to his own legs, side-on to the cooling furnace.

'Go on,' said the bald man. 'Show's over. Buzz off.' He stuck his hands in the back pockets of his jeans and jerked his rosy skull in the direction of the ladder.

'I don't know where I am,' said Raymond. He shuffled his feet in the grey dust of the floor. 'Which is the way?' They would cast him aside: and there was no one left in the world but these two men.

'Go on – get out,' said the man in the blazer. He bent down and picked up a long piece of wood. Raymond flinched, but without even looking at him the man shoved the head of the rake through the furnace door and began to drag it harshly across the shelf where the bones and ashes lay. The bald man leaned his chin on his companion's shoulder and plunged his eyes deep into the oven where the final disintegration was taking place: the ash tumbled down, as the teeth of the rake ground back and forth. It tumbled down through the grille and crumbled into the underchamber.

'Where do I go?' said Raymond. He felt the words cross his lips, but the voice was a child's. 'How do I get home from here?'

The bald man could not extricate his attention from the graceful behaviour of the ashes. He spoke absently, staring into the furnace where the other man's rake was accomplishing its task. 'Don't bother,' he said. He sighed. Then, with the slow resoluteness of a dreamer waking, he lifted his chin and turned on Raymond eyes as inhuman, blank and depthless as those of a figure carved in granite.

'Home,' he said, 'is the last place you need to go. Don't even go back for your things.' He flexed his arms and shoulders, and let them drop. The ripple of it ran down his torso. His joints were oiled with wakefulness.

Raymond stared. He hung on his own breath. 'Who are you?' he whispered. 'What's your name?'

'None of your business,' said the man. 'But you know where to find me now. I'm always here. Always on duty.'

Raymond feasted his eyes on the man: his dark limbs, his worn boots, his shining ivory skull. He felt a terrible urge to approach. He longed to offer his forehead to the touch of the bald man's tattooed hand. Appalled, he saw his own grubby foot move out into the narrow space between them; but without taking a step the man was suddenly beyond his reach, balancing easily on the ladder with one arm raised to the latch of the high trapdoor.

'You'll be all right,' said the bald man in his low, scraping voice. 'Things'll be different now. Just get out of here and start walking.'

He opened the trapdoor with a quick twist of his upstretched hand, and leaned back from the ladder to make room, resting on Raymond his calm stone gaze.

The raking stopped.

Raymond stood in the dust and looked up.

An unbearable diamond of evening sky hovered over his head, scalloped and sprigged at its edges by dark foliage. Air gushed through it, smelling of cut grass; and out of the fresh leaf-masses there poured down on him a light, nervous, persistent whirring, a multitudinous soft tapping and chewing, a vast and infinitesimal cacophony of insects living, living, living.

Raymond shut his mouth. He reached for the jamb with both hands, planted his feet – one, two – on the steep steps and, helped by a violent shove in the small of his back, hauled himself, flailing, through the shrubbery and out on to the staggering lawn.

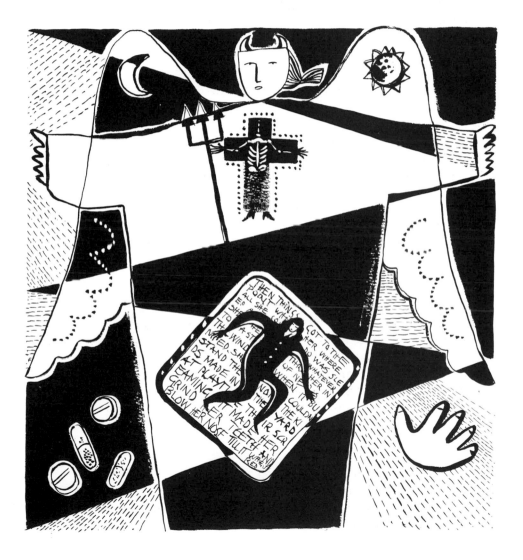

ELIZABETH SMITHER
Two Poems

A Small Potato Crop

In the tiny square garden
– Handkerchief-size transferred to earth –
My gloved hand touches – earth gloves
Thicker as the garden is wide –
Small white clear shapes of a potato crop.

They come from the soil not
As I had imagined, drawn
From mire to air, like a potato birth
But clear, almost jokingly, jovial
As though they bounced up, fair

As a clutch of yellow-haired girls
Who have been playing in pinafores
Before a photograph and fallen into
The developing fluid: the sort of dirty
Called 'clean dirt', noble, upright

A blemish on otherwise faultless humans
Or shoes polished like a guardsman's
That receive the spatter of horses' hooves
Under which baptism of earth and water
It is possible to see their morals gleaming.

The Family Name

From Boston my mother gets
An envelope marked Hurry
Send by return post your subscription
For a family history of the Harringtons.

Once it was a minor castle
Near the Lake District needing donations
The demesne of a knight and lady
Whose pile threatened to tumble.

In Northants once we found
A knee-high signpost: *Harrington*
In front of which we posed, two scions
In a ditch, travelling cross-country.

But my favourite Harringtons are
The two mentioned by Jane Austen
In *Pride and Prejudice*, Chapter Thirty-nine
Who, without any detail, sound pleasant.

BARBARA ANDERSON
The Grateful Dead

First thing I remember knowing was not a lonesome whistle blowing, nor a young 'un's dream of growing up to ride. First thing I remember knowing was that my father liked my mother a lot but my mother didn't like my father. Hardly at all, not even at Christmas.

'Not *another* stupid vase,' she muttered, poking an angry finger at a large vase-shaped parcel wrapped in red-and-green paper with reindeer.

I put my hand on her knee. 'It'll be nice, Mum,' I said. 'Mum?'

My mother was beautiful.

'You're a lucky girl, you've got the prettiest mum in town,' the butcher told me, the liver in his hand bleeding tears of blood on to the sawdust beneath. He slammed an inadequate piece of paper on to the scales, laid the liver to rest and peered at the reading. Both hands stroked the skirt of his striped apron, leaving tracks.

'Wouldn't mind a number two then, Fred?' enquired the baker who had popped in from next door for a nice bit of shin on the bone.

Fred grinned at the baker and winked at me to show that the baker was a caution and I mustn't mind. I didn't. Like much in life, the baker was inexplicable.

I imagined the butcher choosing his weekend joint with care; furrowed brow, lips pursed, pork fingers clutching the edge of the chilled cabinet as he leant over to choose from the rosy rounds of beef, the amputated legs of lamb. How did he recognise the very best one of all? Even better, presumably, than the one he saved each week for my mother. Marbled flesh I knew about, but what were the other signs of grace?

'Are you going to be as pretty as your mum when you grow up?' asked the man who made Christmas candles in his shed at the back. I had called in for some red ones on the way home. I laughed once more to show I knew it was a joke and didn't mind, but I was full of doubts.

My father was interested in grammar. He said I didn't have any. He sat at one end of the table and told me not to say 'got'. 'I have ten biscuits, not I have *got* ten biscuits.'

I was allowed only one biscuit but knew the fact was irrelevant.

My mother sat at the other end of the table and said nothing. Her hair was coiled around her head. There was not a hair out of place.

'Your mother never has a hair out of place,' marvelled the ladies in the town.

'I know,' I said with pride. I watched her doing it. Brushing and brushing then both hands snatching to twist, slam, bang and stick with pins as though she hated it.

I longed for plaits. 'Please, Mum, please.'

My mother said plaits were untidy. They came undone.

I put posies of rosebuds and gypsophila on her dressing table. I was good at posies. I won a prize in the Children's Section at the A and P Show. My daisies and cornflowers with red geraniums for contrast sat in a regulation vase in the Produce Shed alongside a stiff yellow card. Highly commended, it said.

My father played bowls. Bowls made him happy, even the thought of bowls made him smile. He forgot about 'got' on Saturdays and ran down the concrete drive in long white trousers and white shirt and white shoes with no heels because of the turf surface, his bowls in a domed case and gladness in his heart.

He met Mr Duras at the bowling club and brought him home. Mr Duras was hail-fellow-well-met. He said so himself, in our living-room.

'Call me D,' he said, holding out arms which I avoided.

How could I call him D? He was grown up and unknown. And how did you spell D?

Mr Duras made jokes and my mother and father laughed as the late-afternoon sun fell through the plane trees and warmed their backs.

'Shall we have a drink?' said my father, looking at my mother to see if it was all right. My mother nodded. Not a hair moved.

Mr Duras sprang to his feet. 'Good thinking,' he cried. 'Let me help you, Douglas. Can I call you Doug. Let me help.'

'No no,' said my father, 'you keep Ella happy.' My father asked Mr Duras and my mother what they would like to drink and Mr Duras looked happier than ever and said, 'Brandy, thanks, Douggie. And ginger ale.'

My mother said she would have one too why not and I sat on the floor and coloured in the pictures in *Flower Fairies of the Spring* with my crayons because my mother said I could. I never went over the edge even when doing the hard parts like turning the eyes of the Dandelion Fairy blue.

Mr Duras came after bowls and sometimes during the week. He gave my father lifts to bowls and then had to bring him back. 'Beauty,' said Mr Duras as he slammed the door shut on my father's side and ran round to his side of the de Soto. 'Beauty.' My father called Mr Duras Mr Beauty for a joke but my mother didn't laugh so my father stopped.

I ran up the hill to my grandfather's, an oversized Little Red Riding Hood bearing gifts. I took bits of pudding in plastic bowls with frilled plastic hats to stop them spilling, left-over bits of casserole, slices of meat on a covered plate. All these I took in a flat basket so they wouldn't spill. If the puddings were sloshy I walked.

The smell of Lysol was evident long before you saw the monkeys in their cage in the zoological gardens next to the men's lavatory on Bluff Hill. The monkeys took no notice of me and my basket. They were small with bright-pink behinds and they curled side by side and hid their eyes behind their arms when they were not leaping about shrieking, or hunting in each other's fur for fleas with long snapping fingers.

'It'd be a million times easier if he'd live with us,' my mother told people about her father. 'All this endless ferrying of food. There's plenty of room but he won't. You know what they're like,' said my mother.

My grandfather played Harry Lauder records on his old wind-up gramophone and laughed. 'Stop y'tickling, tickle ickle ickling. Stop y'tickling, Jock,' squealed Harry Lauder as the tears ran down the tracks on my grandfather's face.

'Won't you come and live with us, Grandad?' I begged.

He shook his head and reached for his smelly old pipe from the ashtray with shells on it. 'Not likely,' he said. 'Not likely.'

I stopped on the way home to check on a flowering *Magnolia stellata* in a garden near our house. I liked the thick, torn-paper petals, the furry grey of the tight buds, the heavy scent.

Mr Duras was sitting by himself on a wooden seat beside the bus stop.

'Hello, D,' I said, proud of my casual use of Mr Duras' Christian name, if it was.

A bud brushed the brim of Mr Duras' hat as he jumped.

'Hello,' he said.

'What are you doing here?'

Mr Duras coughed. 'I like these things' smell,' he said.

Perhaps I had got Mr Duras wrong. I sat down beside him. He took my hand. I removed it.

'Don't say anything about seeing me here, eh, girlie?'

'Why not?'

'It's our little secret. You like secrets, I bet. All little girls like secrets,' said Mr Duras, jumping about on his bottom with excitement.

I hated secrets. Secrets were exclusion.

'All right.' I stood up. 'I've got to go now, Mr Duras.'

He nodded. 'Don't forget,' he called after me as I belted with my empty basket down Shakespeare Road to the end.

Mr Duras appeared as usual on Saturday to pick up my father. We had had a scratch lunch, my mother called it. Cold meat and pickles and bread because she had been making chutney all morning and had had it up to here with the sight of food. The house sang with the scent of spices.

'Pickle factory,' snorted my mother.

She was standing halfway up a small stepladder stowing the full jars away when Mr Duras arrived. 'Beauty,' he said, clapping his hands as he often did when he said it. 'Beauty.'

My mother's smile, even to Mr Duras, was brief. 'And who's going to hand them up?' she said, snatching a warm shining jar of peach chutney from my father's outstretched hand.

'I will, Mum,' I cried, pink with excitement at the thought.

My mother laughed. I had been known to drop things.

My father looked miserable.

Mr Duras knew my father had a needle match at two. He had a solution. He saw it in a flash. He handed his car keys to my father. 'Take the de Soto, Douggie,' cried Mr Duras. 'I'll walk round when I've handed up this lot. Do me good, lovely day. Lovely.'

'No, no, no,' said my father. 'I'll take the Dodge, but if you could give Ella a hand with this lot, that'd be grand.' He slapped Mr Duras on the shoulder. 'Thanks, D.'

'Bye-bye, darling,' he said.

'Goodbye,' said my mother.

I watched my father out the window. He ran, hopping and skipping down the drive, the domed bag swinging in his hand. 'Bye,' he called again.

Mr Duras and my mother were silent. My mother smiled down at Mr Duras whose hand was on her leg.

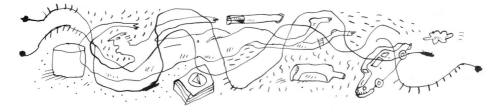

BERNADETTE HALL
Two Poems

Drawing a Conclusion on a Paper Dart

such is the language
of exigency

you wash & cut
& core yellow pears

you could do
with a pig

white & cool
as ointment

the lawn is
littered with them

Miriama

i. On crossing the border, I always
change my name. A simple precaution
& you to guard my back.
                                    Maheno, Monte
Cristo, Waianakarua, Mt. Misery & all
the wild flowers.
                            I am heavy with loot
& disappointment, heading south again down
the soft underbelly of the island, shedding
skins like Coke cans on the Kilmog
& already the rain.

ii. You are waiting, with or without
my blessing, in a blue room of pictures
torn from magazines:
                                Mother Teresa, Athena's
sandalled Victory, a sequoia forest, an avocado
pear, gazelles, two babies in a bath with a chimp,
Ayr's Rock by sunset, Hare Krishnas in their
old gold, mud pools, a street kid.
                                        You have
a bruise on your cheek.

iii. 'Sit down & I'll tell you a story.

At Moeraki in the old days lived a prophet,
Kiri Mahi Nahina who taught all the people that
Tiki had made them, not Io.
                                Te Wera, the warrior,
struck him down with his taiaha. Plugged his eyes,
ears, nose, mouth, anus with moss to contain
the heresy. Then he & his warriors ate him.'

216

iv. Nothing is high, nothing is low, nothing
is hidden.

      This is the song, Miriama, you sing,
doublestopping on my heartstrings.

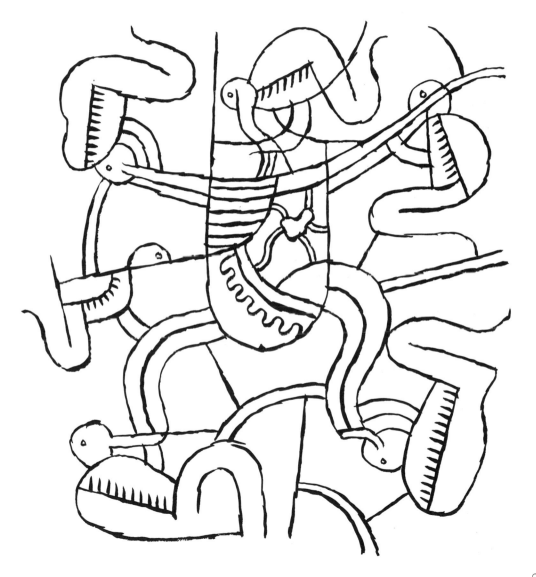

JOAN LONDON
The Angry Girl

You understand, on these excursions we do not often see faces from the old life. Faces from the mainstream, moving swiftly, turned towards us: they catch our eye like mirrors, faces we used to know.

We saw Agnes on a street we didn't know existed. It's as though we live in another city now. Now we go where the others go.

It was an old street not far from the centre of the city, but complete, with its own post office and factories and cafés. Late afternoon, it opened out to us along the footpath like a little foreign town that only appears in this hazy, nonchalant light. At that hour, just as the paper boys set off, just as the hometime buses banked up at the stoplights, Agnes, as if appointed, stepped out of a laundromat and turned our way.

I swear she saw us.

Did I look down? For in that moment I saw my frayed cuffs around my weathered wrists, and Amy's hand loose upon her lap.

A group of highschool girls spilled out from the back door of a bus. They dumped their heavy bags across the footpath and lit up cigarettes and tossed their hair.

Excuse me girls, if we could just . . .

By the time they parted for us, calling out to one another as if across great distance, it seemed the street had darkened, it was evening, and Agnes was not there.

Perhaps it's true that we've become a shadow. People move round us, past us, but they do not look at us. Perhaps they see us only as an outline that has lost its human shape. As carriers of darkness.

After all, don't we come out only with the light? And aren't these excursions our only true existence?

I thought this, late that night, after we'd seen Agnes.

I went to pick up Amy at the usual time next day. Morning tea. If you time it right there's just the echo of the trolleys down the empty corridors. I try to slip my entries and departures into these pauses in routine.

Amy's grey head was turned away on her pillow.

'She's had a bad night,' Verna McIntosh said. 'She needs to sleep.'

Amy lay so still her eyelids quivered with the effort.

'Looks like you've got the day off!' Verna said.

Verna's from the country – fifty years on the same farm. Even here her face is splashed vivid with freckles. Her freckled hands shook as she reached for the teapot on her tray.

'Go on, have a cup.'

'No thanks, Verna.'

Far away, as in a school, a piano started up.

One of Verna's virtues is that she doesn't mind silence. Sometimes I've come into the silence in that room she shares with Amy and felt I've interrupted something.

'See you tomorrow,' Verna said.

I think she knows that in that place I can neither eat nor drink.

The creepers have grown so long they reach out tentacles across the yard and pick out what they want. They have made the studio their nest.

Meanwhile, someone in the neighbourhood has broken the heart of a dog. If you listen long enough the cries lose meaning. They become the peals of a sea mammal recorded underwater. Long echoes from the depths, beyond melancholy, beyond understanding.

A day off.

In the end, if your house is not your home, where do you go? In the end I took the old route across the lawn. I went to visit Rose.

Rose cried, but Rose has always cried, a little every day. Tears seep and swirl around her large brown irises, but stay contained.

'I knew you'd come. Eventually.'

All tears are for oneself, I used to tell her. You are a hard man, she used to say.

She is all in black, with her hair pulled back. Her lips are as pale as her face. Without a word she leads me to the couch, brings me cake and liqueur, sinks, straight-backed, at my feet.

'*What* are you doing with your life?' she says at last. 'Have you seen yourself recently?'

She has caught me off my guard. Is there cake smeared on my face? Did I shave this morning? Am I slouching on her couch now like some old tramp who finds himself in clover?

'You've become a shadow of yourself.'

I wipe my mouth, take a sip of liqueur. I recognise it of course. Smell the berries, smell the honey! Rose would cry. Smell my country in the summer . . . Boris gave it to her. Boris gave her a new bottle each year.

'I know – I *know* – what you've been through . . .'

It's all history now, the rituals and the celebrations. The nostalgia.

'But you can't just throw your life away.'

I look around the room. The sheen has worn off the panelling, I notice, and the chandeliers are coated with candle grease. The lace curtains have started to fray. The room of my nostalgia, Rose called it. The room that Tony built for her. Well, it needed to crumble a little to be more authentic. It suits a little seediness.

'I must be on my way.'

'Forgive me,' Rose says at the door through tears. 'There's no one else to tell you now.' I see the skin drawn back from her face like soft white paper. She takes my hand. 'We have to look after ourselves,' she says, 'now we are old.'

All tears are for oneself. I'm still hard on her, I'm leaving again. *We saw Agnes yesterday.* Is that what I'd come to tell her? Ah Rose, guilt flutters around you but I'm not going to make you to blame.

Perhaps I wouldn't recognise myself. It changes you, this life. We've taken to wearing hats, soft cloth hats that I can pull out of my bag. I've found an airline bag is best for these excursions: for the coats and drinks, the rug, the knife. I like to wear loose clothing now, to feel the air upon my limbs. When I first put my gardening trousers on they fell straight down again. I simply took my knife and cut my belt in half. I'm always walking now. This life has made me thin.

Sometimes as I get dressed I think of Tony, in the soft grey workshirt made for him by Agnes. I see the collar buttoned at his slender throat. His deftly rolled-up sleeves.

Once I thought I was old. Tony and Agnes were living with us then. I couldn't sleep. I lay all night in this room where I am lying now, where the creeper taps against the window. For the first time I saw how late the light burned in their studio.

A twig blazed, I woke. Some children shouted on the road. A whole day had passed without me in it and I did not care. I felt my old teeth raw-edged and heavy in my mouth. I did not want to get up. I did not want anything. I thought: this is how it is to be old.

Agnes came into the kitchen. I saw her crouch in the light of the open fridge and peck at something, fingers to mouth.

I struggled to sit up. 'Yes, that's right, Agnes,' I called out. My voice creaked, strangely urgent. 'I know you are hungry.' She left at once, as though she had not heard.

After that I got up. I put on the kettle and the light. I cleaned my teeth. They did not look too bad. I am the same as I have ever been, I told myself into the mirror. It is not true that we grow old. It is all in the mind. It is not true that we grow wise and repent of our sins! It is not true that we die.

Rose's brother Boris knew that we died. Boris believed in the body, not the mind.

'All belief is just a neurological state,' he said, soon after we first met him.

'Oh, don't listen to him,' Rose said. 'I have argued with him all my life. The man of science. Can you imagine? My little brother was always going to be a doctor. And I was going to be an artist.' She waved her hand around her newly finished room. This was the first of the dinners, the first of Rose's celebrations.

But Agnes, sitting next to him, seemed shocked.

'Don't you believe in moral choice?'

'A theological invention.'

'Or love?'

'Culturally programmed. A name. Different oxygen levels feeding the brain. Different chemicals in the blood.'

'Then you are saying we are prisoners of our bodies.' Beneath the glittery wings she had painted on her cheekbones she appeared quite distressed.

'There are plenty of other opinions on the matter, Agnes,' Amy said.

But Boris put his hand on Agnes's arm.

'Convince me otherwise!' he said. 'Every day the evidence grows more overwhelming. Prescribe a different chemical and you have a different emotional state. Watch me, Agnes! Watch me change my chemical state. In ten minutes or so I will believe in all sorts of possibilities.'

We watched him pour himself a glass of wine and fill up Agnes's glass.

'I am waiting to be convinced.'

We watched his pale deliberate hands, dust-dry across the knuckles. Rose had told us that the theatre sisters said he had the most wonderful hands. She believed it was because their mother was a seamstress in the old country.

It's true that we are prisoners of our bodies. Who would know that better now than Amy? Am I a prisoner too, as I walk behind her? Yet now that I know our course is inevitable, why do I walk with such purpose?

'Here's to Tony,' Rose said. 'A craftsman of genius. An interpreter of dreams.'

Tony, at the head of the table, smiled but kept on watching the shadows of the candles as they flickered across the panelling and the high domed ceiling. Rose turned to me.

'I hope you realise your son is a genius.'

'You've been a great encouragement to him, Rose.'

'It is very important to be encouraged. I was not. When we came to this country I had to go to work. I escaped into marriage. I'd lost faith in myself.'

'What did you want to do?'

'Paint. But I had lost my subject. My father was a jeweller. He used to work in a room like this, with the snow falling outside the window. You'd think a jeweller might have known that we were leaving behind our greatest treasure.'

'Didn't you find new ones?'

'Nostalgia is my art form now. And people.' She smiled around the table. 'I find the people to give shape to my memory.'

When Rose first walked in the streets of this city, the buildings seemed to tower above her, she once told me, although our city is not considered high. But as she found her bearings, the streets pulled back and the buildings flattened out.

I think about this now when I walk with Amy down the streets that we didn't know existed. Do we have more time now to speculate on spires, attics, upper balconies? The buildings rise up beside us, their windows glittering. We are always looking up. We are always checking out the sky.

Rose put on music, horns and pipes, heraldic, like shepherds calling across hillsides. She held her hand out to Agnes. They stood together in the middle of the room. The music quickened into a polka. They faced each other, businesslike, and bowed. They passed shoulders and came together again with tiny trotting steps. They cocked their heads and gave each other long combative glances. With the tips of their fingers touching they turned and turned beneath their arms. Agnes's strange little satin dress moved round her like a pair of crumpled hips. Suddenly they broke away and sat down again, laughing. Rose leaned across to Tony.

I like your wife. She turned to Agnes. Tears filled her eyes.

'You are my younger self,' she said.

Once, a long time later, towards the end, Rose left her house and came to our door, asking to see Agnes. Agnes was in the studio, sewing. Rose made her way across the yard, towards the distant whirr of the sewing machine. A few minutes later Agnes came flying into the house, crying out to Amy that she thought she had swallowed a needle.

Rose had seated Amy at the end of the table, facing Tony. 'The artist's mother,' Rose said, helping her into her chair like an old lady. Amy hardly spoke. She could not speak in someone's house if she did not want to be there.

In the hall as we arrived, Rose had suddenly cried out, 'Amy! There's something on your skirt! A spot! I think it's grease.'

'Must be from my bike,' Amy muttered.

But Rose knelt at Amy's feet, vigorously scrubbing at her hemline. Beneath the hall light Amy hunched her shoulders. It was everything she hated, fuss, attention, being trapped. A stranger's touch.

What Amy does must be of her own choosing. The door is closed: you are on one side of it or the other. Inside, the curtains are drawn but softly moving. There are no words, only this sure breathing. The curtains blow apart for a moment. The light briefly flares.

I can't help thinking that Agnes is going to come to find us soon. That she thinks about us too, now that she has seen us. I imagine how it runs across her mind, our shadow on the street, and is dismissed. And comes back. I imagine how she'll wake up one morning and know what she must do. It's as if I know it's going to happen. Agnes is going to find her way back to Amy.

Boris questioned Agnes.

'Rose tells me you make films.'

'I've made one film.'

'Tell me about it.'

'Oh well, it's about a man getting up in the morning. Going to work. That's all. It isn't very long. It's called *Spirits of the Day*.'

'Where can I see it? Is it showing at the moment?'

'No. It isn't a commercial film.'

'Could I hire it?'

'I have a copy you can borrow if you like.'

'If I borrowed it and showed it to some friends of mine, would you come? I have some friends who are very interested in film. We could have a party afterwards!'

Later he said, 'You're very modest, Agnes. You don't try to promote your work. You don't drink much. You don't sit back and relax into your chair. You don't go in for pleasure, do you?'

'Yes, I do.' Agnes lifted up her head. 'Pleasure of a particular kind.'

Her face caught the light and I saw her as she lifted up her head on the way to work in the studio every morning. I saw that as if for the last time.

I felt the light on my face too as I leapt up, waving my knife. The light seemed to come from the yellow liqueur that Rose had poured into my glass, that spread around your throat, sweet enough to make you choke. We discussed choking.

'There is only one thing to do!' I cried, leaping up, the rescuer, the man with the knife. I stationed myself behind Amy. I took her chin in my hand, pushed back her head, placed the knife-edge against her gullet.

'Just here,' I said, 'so as to avoid the jugular.'

'Could you really do that?' Rose asked.

Amy, released, took a sip of water without looking at me.

'What do you think?' Agnes said to Boris. 'Would he kill her, or save her life?'

What did Tony see as he looked around that room? A collection of angles, joins, materials, problems posed and solved? Or was he aware of being in a space quite separate from himself now, a new space, every moment further from the cast of his hands, Rose's memory?

All the same, he must have been a romantic, to create a room like that.

The moon is up, shining at a sixty-degree angle through the creepers at my window, full on to my face as I lie here in the darkness. On such a night ... I could go there now, make my way up the silent corridors. It's me, I would whisper over her bed, I have something to show you.

You might say I set up the scenes, choose the light, appropriate the movies. Bestow my moments ... Oh, don't think this doesn't cross my mind. Don't think I differentiate myself. That all along I haven't known about the workings of desire.

I want to take her to a place where we can watch the moon roll its own huge course. Turn with it, watching, until something on the edge of the horizon is about to cross its path. Wait for it, that moment, see it getting closer, see the tip of that waving branch, waiting. Wait for it, wait ... *There.*

The moon hung low over our roof as we walked home that night. We walked in a procession across the lawn, Amy, Tony, Agnes, I. Like workers returning to our quarters. Like tired performers.

'Boris is very like his sister,' I called out to Agnes. 'A patron of the arts.'

Agnes muttered something.

'What's that, Agnes?'

'He's a *layman*,' Agnes said.

I should have made some gesture. I should have tried to catch her, hold her, so she didn't slip away. Shown her somehow that I knew that she was there. Perhaps she only ever saw us as shadows closing in on her. I should have thought more quickly, seen more clearly . . . But a schoolgirl kept getting in the way.

For a long time I did not think Agnes's film was very good. It seemed amateurish to me: all those shots of the same subject from different angles, like a home movie! It seemed disjointed, it did not tell a story. Just the things a man – Tony – does in the morning. So what? I thought, secretly. It did not come to a conclusive ending. I felt sorry for her after all that effort. I did not speak of this to anyone amongst the general acclaim. To my surprise she won a grant to make a second film.

In the end I asked Rose why she thought it was so good.

'Because something seems to grow in it,' she said. 'Because it stays.'

It's true that sometimes now in the morning I see the lines and shapes and shadows in the courtyard that she filmed Tony watching from the studio. A whole architecture seems to be streaming upwards. For a moment it's as if I see what Tony saw.

Or how Agnes saw him. He is never less than elegant. I see him buckling on his belt, with his hammer and his ruler and his leather pouch. I see him taking out his pencil, bending to write something, a note or list. Printing rather than writing: he never was at home with writing. He chews his cheek a little, wistful, as he bends.

I see him looking in the mirror before he shaves, rubbing his hand over his cheek with something like anguish. There is a sense of a secret held within each scene, which she lets stay secret. When I see Tony now I see him in the film. Perhaps that's why I didn't like it. She knew more about him than I did.

*   *   *

How did she look? *Small*, a small figure on the scale of the street. Small as a celebrity looks small when seen in real life. She stepped out of a laundromat carrying a suitcase. There was something in her other hand. A box? Soap powder? In the suitcase would be her clothes, freshly washed and dried, still warm. Her sheets, her towel.

Her hands were full, it was not possible to wave.

She did not seem small when we first met her. She was seventeen, a year older than Tony. He brought her home from a bus after he had lent her a fare. They were sitting at the kitchen table: they always sat at the kitchen table. Everything about her then seemed in danger of spilling over, her ash, her can of Coke which she kept sliding round the table, the T-shirt bulging over her school skirt, even the blood rising to a flush in her cheeks. She kept wrapping and unwrapping her large pale legs around the legs of her chair. We sipped our tea on the edge of our own chairs. The room seemed full of smoke and school bags and a hectic intimacy.

'Good tea deserves the very best treatment,' she read out from our packet of Darjeeling. 'Oh, haha. Oh very true.' Her hands trembled on the packet. She looked us in the eye. 'Don't mind me.'

I was pleased that Tony had a caller, I did not remind him of his homework. I hoped that he might make a friend. There was a distance between us then, and in that space I could see only emptiness. Anyone might move in.

'Friendship takes effort,' I had told him. I did not consider that he made enough effort with anything. He wore his hair long and spread his long legs out on the couch, hour after hour, watching TV. Other people, other people's children, seemed pulled in their lives by invisible strings. But for Tony, I thought, I have to pull the strings.

I bent down over him, gathered his hair in my hands. 'It is not even fashionable!' I said. *But it is beautiful*, a voice crossed my mind. I saw my hand pressing down and down on the nape of his neck. *Life, real life!* I shouted at him, at this child who had never once raised his voice to us. God knows what I thought I was sacrificing him to.

I was waiting for an angel to stop me.

I think of Tony now, if he were here. How deftly, how naturally he would care for Amy. How he would whistle, take his time. How I would prize it now, his unconcern for time, or time's irony.

Above all, I think of the pleasure she would have, just in looking at him.

*   *   *

I liked to look at Tony when he sat with Agnes. He sat away from her, with his chair turned just a fraction towards her, his back to the window. You were always aware of the space he made around him. When he looked at Agnes his eyes went still with concentration. As a child, I knew, he could fall in love with something he saw, the way the ears sat on a dog, the ring on his mother's hands, an unshaved stretch of cheek that he would stroke with an almost unbearable affection.

Agnes came often. It seemed she was always in trouble. She lived with her father and was supposed to look after him. And to go to church on Sundays, her national church. She climbed out her bedroom window to go to clubs at night. Once her father beat her.

I listened and shook my head, like a good parent, like a parent who believes you must never do violence to your child.

What is her house like? we asked Tony. He said it smelt of pickles and cement. Her father was always renovating: he had filled in his entire yard with concrete. There was horror in his voice when he said this.

We gave her a chocolate egg at Easter. She ate it straight away at the table, very quickly, as if she were by herself. She did not thank us. Afterwards she kept sneaking up a finger to check out the corners of her mouth. Any little kindness seemed to disconcert her. But we learnt later that she always took account of what had been given to her.

We asked her what she was going to do when she left school.

'Would you believe – acting? *This* week. But first I have to go away.'

We missed her when she went.

Perhaps they should never have lived with us. Perhaps the family track, played too long, wears too deep, wears out. Perhaps it was an indulgence for us all.

Tony was seduced by the chance to build his own space. He made the studio a box of many tiny parts to contain his life with Agnes. He built her a darkroom hardly bigger than a cupboard, disguised by sliding wooden panels. In the morning we could see their two heads propped up in their deep bed beneath the window.

Agnes filmed him building the studio. Later she would use some of this in *Spirits of the Day*. Agnes was thin now and held her shoulders high as she crossed the courtyard. She was careful with herself, after all those years away, as if she knew herself to be delicate. She did not smoke. She used our bathroom to take long hot baths.

She did not like to be away from Tony for too long. If he watched TV with us she would come and stand for a moment by the door. He always went. I don't know what pacts they had made.

I see us now as we walked back in the procession from Rose's house that night. The moon hung low, the spires and towers of the distant city were bright as if the night were day. As if the daytime world had been a dream and we had woken up and were returning now. Returning to our dream of home.

I became aware that Agnes was not sleeping. I saw the light burning in the studio like a lamp ceaselessly tended. Even if the light was off, I felt I saw her wakefulness rising like a shadow in the window. I realised that I too was not sleeping, or how would I know this?

She said that she was worried about the new film. The film was to be about her father, about coming to a new country. About coming to a point of acceptance. It was to be called *Regions of the World*. She knew the ending, the final scene. Her father is repairing the roof of his house. Suddenly he straightens up and looks out all around him. Like an old king he makes his survey of the world.

But she didn't know how to get to that point. She found herself unable to approach him, even to visit him. The images she had worked out so far were all of absence. His absence, from her. She was wondering if this was really of importance. If she was not just inventing a false epiphany. If she was not just being indulgent.

'Why aren't you working, Agnes?'

'Because I hate myself.'

'Why do you hate yourself?'

'Because I'm not working.'

'Nothing else is real to me.'

'Agnes, this is also real.'

'Nothing else can make me happy any more.'

'What about a hot bath?'

'It's too late for me!' She flapped her hands about her head as if to frighten off a circling bird. 'It's got me. It's too late for me now.'

In the afternoons she went out. The day loosened, waved its boughs around, grew tawdry. Rose's laugh was brittle, her eyes tearful if I visited. 'I must ask Tony and Agnes for drinks again, very soon, all of you.' She did not mention Boris.

I believe she met him nearly every day.

I sat up all night with Agnes's father, Andrzej, waiting for news of her. By dawn he had grown familiar to me, not by talking, but by my sensing his movement across the room. His sighs, his momentary snores, the heavy shifts of his body resembled my own. At dawn we drank a glass of whisky each to the intermittent song of birds.

'She was always angry,' he said. His face was grey, like mine. Its lines did not look like those of a tyrant or a bully to me, but of ordinary failure. 'Such an angry girl.' He blinked back tears.

Verna shook her head at me again this morning. Amy did not stir. 'Too tired,' Verna said. 'Not today.'

She's always shy with me at first. She does not look at me as I pull the ramp down and then lock the chair in next to my seat in the van. I've learnt to stop myself from saying, *There we go! That's it!* I've learnt I mustn't look at her as we set off. Her eyes gaze steadily to her left, away from me. *Grant me this much*, it's as if she says.

First thing, we might go to the park. The grass is white-capped with papers, boxes, cans, tiny bleached chicken bones. A brisk wind lifts a thousand seagull feathers towards us. There is a sense of aftermath. It's as good a place as any from which to start.

A day has its own rhythm. *Left or right?* I ask Amy. *North or south? Stay here or move on?* Her nod is always very sure. There seems to be a path to follow if only we can find it. On good days we move as if we're getting closer to something.

We like the backlands. We like quarries, railway sidings, beaches tucked in between factories. Washing dancing on solitary lines. We like old streets on the outskirts of the city. Old buildings worn and darkened and the gaps between them. Wind blowing down streets like little foreign towns.

We never speak with the others that we meet. Other travellers making their excursions. Drunks and loiterers, lovers, run-aways: those with secret eyes, those with time. Those who carry everything they need with them. Who have left everything behind.

We've never spoken much. I watch her, gauge, assess, offer an adjustment. I want to get it right, but I'm often clumsy. I didn't know about this, about caring for someone. It's not a case of handling, it's a case of becoming one body. I didn't know about this.

Some days we fall asleep. A warm rhythmic sleep that continues the movement of the van. Afternoon sleep, like rooms with open doors, where voices echo as they pass. I wake up hoarse with sentences: *Her damp hair clung to her like feathers*; or once, *They found a black sword buried in her heart.*

Aren't these the best sleeps, Amy? Side by side?

Some days I never get it right. Some days grit flies in our faces, rain falls in large deliberate drops, the endless streets are more than we can bear. Every minute becomes more hopeless. Amy does not pretend. She turns her head and shuts her eyes. We can't wait to be apart. No consolation, anywhere.

We're late, it's five o'clock, the corridors are restless. Room after room, they mutter, sigh, wring their hands at the onset of the night. Verna jolts awake as we enter. 'I haven't got the tea yet,' she cries, 'and the men are coming in.'

The van seems faster, lighter, when I've left her. I drive more recklessly, put on the radio. I catch the last bars of a piece of music.

The night! We haven't tried the nights yet. We haven't made our way yet through the city streets night-lit, through the crowds, the cries and music in the dense electric air. And on, into the shadows between street lamps, into the tracts that have no lights, the plains that end in blackness . . .

I have such plans!

I lie here and I'm driving again across my sleepless landscape.

Is it too early to go yet? My legs move as if already they are pushing something. My hands shake as I pack our bag. Oh my darling, where are you? I feel an end is closing in. Is this what Agnes would have said?

When Agnes went missing, Amy rode her bike around the neighbourhood. I stayed by the telephone. We felt she wasn't far away. Tony had left the week before, without explanation. He left a message with Agnes in the studio. He said to look after her, for him. He said he would be back one day. He never writes of course.

Amy rode and rode. She had to move, she had to be outside, alone. Her face grew very red, she reeled in, dizzy, panting. All the same she went straight to the phone. 'I'm ringing Boris,' she said.

Boris had a cold. He blew his nose, sniffed, put his handkerchief back in his pocket. 'How would I know?' Boris said, sniffing, hunched in a home-knitted jumper. 'How would I know where she goes?'

Amy gave a cry and fell down clutching her head.

I found her. It was when I'd given up that I heard it, a tiny scratching behind the darkroom door.

'I found Agnes,' I whispered over Amy's bed. 'She's going to be all right.'

'Like you,' I whispered. I listened to her breathing.

'She's not here,' Verna McIntosh said. 'She's at the singalong.'

'The what?'

'The singalong. Down the corridor. Hear the piano?'

'I'll go and find her.'

'Why d'you take her out all the time?'

'Because I want her to be happy.'

'But we don't think about being happy any more. We've given up being happy.'

Later she said, 'I used to wait all the time for him to come and get me. I used to think he'd be worried, they'd all be worried, wondering how I was. I used to worry for them. But I've given all that up now. You're on your own here. You're always on your own. That's what that girl said.'

'What girl?'

'The one with the suitcase. The one who came to visit Amy yesterday.'

For a long time after we were married we did not have children. We did not talk about this. We bought ourselves a little white dog called Pup. How well we trained Pup! He walked to heel and sat and came when he was called. Each evening we took him to the park. We thought that it was good for him to run free and mix with other dogs. He took off in all directions, barking, feigning aimlessness. 'Here, Pup!' we called. Our voices mingled in the twilight, not young, not old.

Once Pup, when called, trotted a victor's lap around us. He was carrying a little parcel in his mouth. He laid it at our feet and sat back, at our service. It was a little brown bird with its eyes closed and its wings folded to its sides. Was it dead or only terrified?

I have to calm down, take a breather, get myself ready now. Focus, and yet take everything into account. An end is coming, if not a resolution. I want to get it right.

I think of Tony, if he were here now, how he would set to work, his cheek chewed in concentration. I think of what he'd build for her, the witty skylights, the ramps and balconies, taking her outside, bringing the outside in. If he were here she would have stayed.

Once I knocked with a message on the studio window. I thought that I'd seen Agnes sitting up in bed, but it was Tony, wearing Agnes's nightgown. I went away at once and forgot it, like a dream. Perhaps it was a dream, it doesn't matter. That was what I saw when I looked in that window.

I think of Rose, with her skin drawn back like soft white paper, her hair drawn back in penance, as she bends over the dishes she has prepared. In the house she never leaves, tears fall into the dishes she thinks are my favourites. Tears fall as she keeps my dishes warm.

I think of Agnes, when I turned the darkroom light on. How her outline rushed to take shape in the dim light like a body rising out of water. How her body lay before me, private, sleeping, eyes closed, arms at her side.

I think of Amy, with her head cocked towards the piano and the half-circle of singers pulled up in their chairs. She sits to one side, so she can watch. *On the Wings of a Snow White Dove*, they sing – patiently, dreamily – as if reading the lines in their heads.

She doesn't sing, of course. She is chewing on her cheek, as Tony does, in concentration. Her cocked head seems alert, but patient, not ironic. She doesn't know that I am at the doorway, watching her, waiting for her, at her service. Her eyes are dreamy too. Who knows what she is seeing, what pilgrimage she's making, what landscape she is visiting, what region of the world?

LAUREN HOLDER
We Have Lost a Woman

Around in this garden there are a lot of empty flowers. She must be here somewhere, she must have been here. She must have wanted to be. And that's it, she wouldn't be here, but if someone brought her here, she would never want to go back. But she would say nothing if they brought her back.

I brought her here a few times. The first time, she could walk in tiny shuffling steps with just my motivation to help her. The second time, I had to push her in the wheelchair everyone said she didn't need until someone put her in it and then nobody could get her out. It seemed she had no need for walking any more, I wonder why.

And when she got out into this garden, the garden overwhelmed her and she wouldn't talk to me, it was hard work. I thought up one thing to say and then another but they all sounded strange and out of context. And then she started bird-calling. It seemed she had quite a lot to say to birds, but I don't speak bird so I don't think I know what she was talking about.

If you don't know what someone's talking about, you don't know what they're thinking about, do you? Sitting in the cloudy sky with the green grass bright and swarming at our feet like the starving millions, and the trees pulsing with the conversation of invisible birds, I had some idea, but I couldn't translate it and the information was of no interest to anyone anyway. And then I took her back because she was hard work and she had filled up all the time in the day that I had for her, which was fifty times as much as anyone else had for her and this was an unfortunate thing. She thanked me a hundred times, and she meant each one twice.

The other time I took her out to the garden, I had to push her up the driveway and the tyres were flat on the wheelchair and she weighed as much as two moas. Wasn't there a team of horses for this job? Don't trust me to do it all by myself, I'm not Pop-Eye (the sailor man), gravity will drive her back over me and we will both be dead. But I struggled up against gravity and reached the flat bit and she wasn't worried and soon we were flooded with the smells of a million eager flowers, and they all wanted us to see them and we saw all of them.

She sucked the scent right out of them, she was excessive with them. Her method is very greedy and straightforward, she sticks her nose right in like it's a bee. She is greedy with her food, her manners are indelicate in this area also. But not to condemn her, there is a joy in watching her utilise all her senses, she doesn't waste them. She doesn't ignore them. She loves a good cooked chicken, she doesn't wait for it to go cold (like a lot of the others), she likes to see so she stares, she turns around to have a better look in town and my mother gets embarrassed. She has low self-monitoring, it could be said. She has eyes and a nose for the things around but no ear for social customs.

Once we have emptied the flowers in the hospital's garden, we drive across the road in the wheelchair to use up the council's ones. We throw caution to the wind, we drive like a racing wheelchair, we have become loosened and reckless, powered by the scent of so many gaudy flowers. We make it up the hill of the road easily. She can't reach the roses from her wheelchair this time, there is a moat of earth seeming to guard them from the likes of her so I have to tear them off at the necks and feed them to her.

My brother comes and helps, his jeans reach almost to the top of her white head, his hand arrives out of the blue sky with a different-coloured rose each time and stops at her nose and hovers there like a hummingbird. She takes a lot of feeding. I think this is because she is herself a flower. She acts like a greedy bird but she is only a friendly flower.

This explains too why in her younger and juicier days she would take the kids uptown and we would all be walking around and slightly behind her and she would at some stage not be there. Instead she would be walking down a dark, carpeted tunnel with the colours of dusty burgundy gleaming from a million corners, and then into a large and dark and round room full of tables, at each but one of which would be sitting other people's dusty old aunts. At the table with no aunt at it, there would be a tiny fluted glass with a waist so slender and elongated it was like a neck (I would hesitate to call it a stem for this word belongs to flowers). The glass would be like a star on a stage because a lonely yellow shaft of light would hold it in thrall like a spotlight and it would sparkle with a rich red light, like a lead chorus girl who has a tight round belly full of sherry.

She who we had come with would sit at this table with her green coat still on while we would stand around her, small and many and like her chicks, and watch her hand with the papery skin and tapered fingers wrap itself around the glass and lift it out of the limelight just like King Kong and the girl who kicked. King Kong's hairy hand lifted the girl-glass up to a mouth that was not King Kong's, but was the mouth of a moa, and the beak of a moa would dip into the hand-wrapped crystal glass and all its contents would be sucked into her mouth as if it were going up an escalator in buckets very fast.

And then, and then, she would relax on the chair like a daisy that had opened its petals because at last daylight had broken, and we would take our seats at the table like the small children of a daisy, but our petals were closed because it was dark in there and the colour of old blood was lying on everything.

But now it is time to take her back again for she must be stashed under a roof that is discontinuous with her life. We leave the council's roses but the flowers have bony arms which hold us in thorny, sentimental reluctance until I have the idea to take some with us, so I cut them off at their grabbing hands and decorate her with their fists. I tuck their knobbly wrists into her lapel and into the crevices in her coat and when she is a fully decorated Buddhist shrine and I, as an Indian, am finished with my arranging in the church, I turn the wheelchair around and aim it down the hill.

Thank you, she says, with such vehemence that it stands apart from all other utterances, in a museum-case alone, this is what sincerity sounds like, sounded like.

Released from the council flowers at the top of the driveway, there is nothing to keep us away, except the fact that she would rather stay in the garden, but she doesn't say anything so I don't know exactly and anyway, the garden she really wants to stay in is another garden. One in her past.

I deposit her back into the chair she has in the hospital lounge, she offers no resistance. I feel like I have driven her in in a wheelbarrow, she seems like an uprooted polyanthus with a clod of dirt around her feet, what is a polyanthus doing on that chair? I have driven up in my wheelbarrow and tipped it up on its end and she has fallen out, her yellow petals are papery, she has fallen on her side. She smiles at me from among a community of withered leaves, her smile is like a watery winter sun, I bend down and straighten her up. I ask her if she would like her handbag and of course she would. This is one of the few things we know about her. So I hang the beige handbag, which has not been uptown since it was young, on a furry green leaf and lean into the pale-yellow petals and kiss the face that I find in there goodbye.

And I don't see her again, ever.

MICHAEL ONDAATJE
Breeze

For bp Nichol

Nowadays I listen only to duets.
Johnny Hodges and The Bean, a thin slip
of piano behind them
on this page on this stage
craft a breeze in a horn.
One friend sits back and listens
to the other. Nowadays
I want only the wild and tender
phrasing of 'Nighthawk',
its air groaned out
like the breath of a lover.
Rashomon by Saxophone.
So brother and sister woke, miles apart,
in those nineteenth-century novels you loved,
with the same wound or desire.
We sit down to clean and sharpen
the other's most personal lines
– a proposal of more, a waving dismissal
of whole stanzas – in Lethbridge in Edmonton
you stood with the breeze
in an uncomfortable Chinese restaurant
in Camrose, getting a second cup
at The Second Cup on Spadina.
I almost called you this morning
for a phone number.
Records I haven't yet returned.
Tapes you were supposed to make for me.
And across the country
tears about your death.
I always thought, someone says,

he was very good for you.
Though I still like, Barrie,
the friends who are not good for me.

Along the highway
only the duets and wind fill up my car.
I saw the scar of the jet that Sunday
trying to get you out of the sky.
Ben Webster, Coleman Hawkins.
An A and an H, a bean and a breeze.

All these twin truths

There is bright sumac, once more,
this September, along the Bayview Extension

From now on
no more solos

I tie you to me

B R E E Z E

240

241

IAN WEDDE

Rhetoric, Absence, Elegy:
The Soul of the Family Album

1.

My impulse to write something, or, in other words, to understand something about the family album came from one experience in particular.

The experience was an all-night viewing of colour slides taken by the recently deceased father of a friend. This man had been a taxi-driver in Onehunga, Auckland. The household was part of a large, cohesive working-class clan. My friend's father, the taxi-driver, had had a passion for taking slides of every domestic event of any importance, from the mid-fifties right through to his death from cancer in the mid-seventies – in fact, until after his death, because his family, recognising the importance of the photographs to him, continued to take them on his behalf when his illness prevented him, and went on to record his decline, his funeral, the various wreaths brought by family and colleagues, ceasing only when the record was respectfully and finally complete.

The nine-hour viewing of these slides, beginning one night and ending at mid-morning the next day, was accompanied by my friend's commentary. His memory was able to mesh affectionately with the images that passed in swift succession before us. The combination of his laconic commentary and the rapid substitution of one image for another over a long period of viewing time resulted in a vicarious familiarity. We soon became intimate with key players in this narrative. The family house and its surroundings, for a start. As time passed – at once slowly, like movie sequences frame by frame through an editing machine, and rapidly because in the gaps between 'frames' months or even years may have elapsed – we saw waves of different-coloured paint wash over the house, we saw alterations ('improvements') to it, we saw its drapes change, and the configuration of its surrounding garden obey new fashion instructions. We saw the house itself respond to cultural directives and trends. We saw it respond to the interventions of the children who were growing up in it. We saw a process of education entrained, a process which was a correlative of the household's aspirations for its children. The house itself, now blushing in decorator tones, with a new garage, a concrete-block incinerator instead of a forty-four-gallon drum, and a bean-trellis situated in a vegetable garden progressively less functional and more 'landscaped' – this house, itself an actor in the historical narrative, spoke of the household's class mobility, its desire to 'better itself'; its desire, at least, to see the children better themselves.

We viewed weddings at which betterment was proclaimed both formally, in the rhetorical complexity of the groupings, the magnificence of the breakfast, the sumptuousness of the presents, and informally, in the smiles and other evidences of satisfaction, which the photographs tried to arrange within the formal codes of decorum. And we also viewed occasions, including weddings, at which the non-discriminatory photographer had recorded something more like dissatisfaction: the 'shotgun wedding', with less than splendid rhetoric (for example, smaller groups in the photographs, fewer and less complex regroupings, a narrower range of relationships), with brothers or cousins in hired suits, their expressions required to suppress not grins but scowls.

We saw the Christmas dinner table increase its number of settings over the years. We saw department-store crèches, frosted bells, hollies, Santa Clauses and other table decorations subverted by the tastes of the children who had been encouraged to 'improve' themselves, substituting cut flowers for mock mistletoes, bottles of wine for fizzy drinks, salads, cold cuts, and designer platters for the roasts and puddings of the fifties, linen for the coloured paper serviettes.

An elegiac tone entered the viewing experience. The commentary, seldom less than wry, though never derisive, often had to record a sense of loss. Certain events marked out the interstices of this development. A mighty macrocarpa tree on Mount Pleasant, Onehunga, had to be felled because it was endangering neighbouring houses. This moment was recorded in detail, with photographs of successive loppings, of the groups of neighbours who had assembled to watch. In the context of the extended 'history' of the viewing, of its time both accelerated and arrested, the moment gained an iconic grandiloquence, which the commentary, therefore, barely needed to record.

Other elegiac moments included the children leaving home, having already passed from paper serviettes to linen napkins, from cordial to wine, so to speak – moving out into marriages, careers, and the destinations provided by class mobility and aspiration, by fifties and sixties prosperity, a state education system, and a planet shrunk by information technology until travel seemed a no more exotic possibility than had the arrival of foreign gourmet cuisine on the family Christmas dinner table.

And of course this elegy passed eventually to the record of the final illness and death of my friend's father. The last images were of wreaths. 'That one was from Auntie May . . . that's from the taxi co-op . . . the bowling club . . . bloody old Frank . . . the RSA . . .'

My memory of this viewing has remained vivid into a second decade. And memory not just of the experience as a whole, but of numerous discrete images in it (the macrocarpa tree, for instance); and of what we might call time-lapse images, the result of successions of frames, of time made to pass (for example, the record of changing fashion, of aspiration, of 'development', of generations of bean-trellises, of successive table-settings for Christmas dinner).

When I now investigate this memory, wanting to find out what lies behind my impulse to write about, to understand, such an album, I discover three events. One is that such a domestic record is simultaneously a public one. It offers the miniature domestic model as a test case or sampler of the wider culture. It does this because, intending to record a 'moment' in the family history, it ends up recording the *signification* of that moment: not the occasion simply, but what the occasion encodes, what it allegorises. It is the rhetoric, not the moment, that we remember (though, to be fair, this will be less true for family members themselves). And the main business of the rhetoric is to proclaim an ideal of progress. Recording a moment of family pride (a successful wedding, a graduation ceremony), it encodes a wider social momentum, a drive to betterment, an ideal of class mobility, the *political* model of progress.

This model is of course not a model of class equality but rather a model produced by surplus value in a capitalist growth economy. It is progress driven by the necessity for surplus, and therefore by the need for increased consumption. The successful class war, here, results in better educated, and therefore better paid, consumers. It is the macro-code of economic growth that here directs the micro-code of family aspiration. The conjunctive term, now, is *prosperity*: the album of colour slides taken by my friend's father records the prospering of a family; it does so under the rhetorical banner of 'prosperity', which is of course a political slogan urging consumption as a measure of progress.

The second event I think I discover when I investigate the memory of this marathon viewing is the *absence* of the recordist himself. It seems self-evident enough that, because it was my friend's father who took the photographs, he does not appear in them. Except ritually, on the regular occasions when he bought a new cab (another record of progress administered by prosperity, as well as of automobile design); and on the occasions of his yearly holiday, when there was always at least one snap of him next to the car, in somewhere like Caroline Bay, Timaru; and, finally, on the occasion of his illness and death.

But this self-evident absence raises certain questions when considered in the larger rhetorical terms described above.

Doesn't it, for example, resemble the absence we sense instructing history to smile? Isn't unseen Dad directing the wedding group (or re-group) to smile, very like those directors who encode history? Who edit the images, the language, the texts, by which our recall of the past is administered? Who administer the memory of a culture, and therefore, inevitably, that culture's understanding of its present situation? Isn't Dad the snapshootist a kind of Randolph Hearst, a Murdoch, a Kerry Packer? More to the point, because less endowed with the villainously 'human faced' lineaments of conspiracy and paranoia, isn't Dad like Time Life Inc? Like CBS, NBC? Like those 'agencies' which have commodified information, which offer edited information for sale on the global satellite networks?

Poor old Dad. He thought he was (he was) celebrating the graduation ceremony of his (smiling) son, who would go on to become a record company executive director in New York. What Dad was doing as well was reproducing the directorial absence, the unaccountable invisibility, of those who produce, edit, package, and market 'the news' ('the truth') for his television screen: information which is framed, paced and contextualised by commercials urging him to consume and create the surplus (the profit) which, needless to say, also drives the 'news agencies'.

We can now peep in at a melancholy tableau: the prideful family recordist is seated in the living-room watching television. The room, the television set, the new drapes and coverings on the sofa, he has already recorded with proper satisfaction, if not with the emotion reserved for special occasions such as weddings and graduations. He is watching television. On the screen appear commercials, many of which are directed by the same rhetoric as his own album slides. Their base is the prospering family. They show this family partaking of that consumption which is the benchmark of progress. The television commercials urge consumption as a measure and signification of progress. We are observing a loop, a loop rollered by the drives of growth economy, a loop on which the reflexivities of the album and of the commercial seem to become interchangeable; until it is hard to decide whether Dad is looking at his album, or at commercials, and hard to decide which of the album or the commercial originated the rhetoric which now articulates both.

This melancholy tableau is an exaggeration, even a melodrama; and it is high time we rescued the emotion of the album from the cynicism of the loop – it has never been my intention to belittle the emotional integrity of what my friend's father, and countless other domestic album chroniclers, are up to when they commemorate the momentous in domestic history. Nor does the tableau discriminate fairly between the audiences intended for and created by the album and the commercial respectively.

Nonetheless, the loop exists. A simple illustration of it is provided by a story told me by a friend. This friend, who ran a café, was on good terms with the owners of a dairy near by, where she would go with large orders for emergency supplies. The owners of the dairy were Fijian Indians recently arrived in New Zealand. One day the woman in the dairy showed my friend a photograph: it was of herself dressed in a good sari, standing next to a fridge whose door was open and whose interior was stocked with food. My friend's first thought was that the Indian woman had been asked to be in a commercial, that the photograph was an art-direction still for the ad. In fact (of course) the photograph was a domestic one, taken to be sent to relatives back in Fiji, as evidence of the dairy owners' prosperity in New Zealand. In this image, a seamlessly ingenuous folding together of the commercial and of the album has taken place. We may find it more comfortable to contemplate *this* image, with its obviating rationale of consumer underprivilege, than the image of Dad on the sofa looking at the television's distorted and unaccountably directed reflection of his own family album; nonetheless, both images tell us that the loop exists.

The third event produced by my investigation of the memory of the dead taxi-driver's slide collection is the transformation of that narrative into an elegy.

And not just an elegy for the dead recordist himself, which the viewing occasion, with its wry and affectionate commentary, had become; but for everything overmantled by the progress the dead man had so devotedly recorded. For the interior decorations, and furnishings, and housepaints of my friend's childhood; for the forty-four-gallon drum incinerator, the practical vegetable garden, the bean-trellis against the corrugated-iron fence; the red paper serviettes, frosted crèche, fizzy drinks, and crêpe-paper hats; for the highschool pennants and sporting trophies, the framed diplomas, the graduation scrolls; the tables bedecked with wedding gifts, recorded and enumerated with the prideful pomp of tribute. The first grandchildren, with their grandmother – later, by their grandfather's bedside.

This catalogue is not, I hope, mere nostalgia – especially not class nostalgia, not a sentimental recall of the trappings of a working-class household beginning to prosper in the fifties. My friend's father, after all, was certainly not afflicted with this nostalgia: he was recording not the losses, but the gains; and the on-going disappearing act of his long narrative was, in fact, the precise record of his satisfaction. 'Things were looking up.' 'The past was best forgotten.'

Nonetheless, the effect of the repetitive substitution of a greater advantage for a lesser, of the constant *making invisible* of what the narrative has just finished recording, is to stock the narrative with a dense crowd of phantoms. Haplessly, it becomes as much a record of anachronism as of innovation. It becomes a dirge for what was discarded, as well as a celebration of prosperity's tribute.

To the absence of the recordist we now join the absence of the discards. The recordist, the director who is telling this family history when (and how much) to smile, is present only in those moments of transmission, when a substitution is coming into focus, when a substituted-for is sliding into invisibility. His presence is repetitively signalled by this act, by the act of making one moment replace another, the photograph's signal moment of record. His presence is not indicated by the anachronisms; nor is it in their replacements. He is present only in the exact moment of change, in the instant of transmission recorded by his act of pressing the camera's shutter. It's as though, at every such moment, at all the thousands of them, he inserted himself between the laminates of past and present, between memory and desire.

And what is the function of memory, if not to recall, to reify absence; and of desire, if not to summon the same from the other direction, from the future? And what is this absence, from the laminated centre of which memory and desire are issuing their summons? What is this void in which they stand back to back? It is of course the space where economic surplus exults. Which is precisely why nostalgia can be so successfully pressed into the service of advertising. What is past will whet the appetite for what is to come. And the photograph, with its nearly instantaneous shuttering of time, its insertion of presence between obsolescence and potential, as though between the two surfaces of a colour slide, provides that moment's ideal record. That is why photography and advertising are inseparable. It is also why we greedily follow the narratives of photograph albums – why we were compelled to watch nine hours of slides taken by my friend's father. Why even that elegy was appropriated to appetite.

Rhetoric, absence, and the elegy: the three reasons (as I discovered) why I wanted to write something (understand something) about the album and the snapshot. Three banners under which to advance into a viewing of my own dead father's enormous collection of slides.

2.

This was something I'd wanted to do ever since my father's death ten years ago, more pressingly since my mother's death four years later. Now there was an occasion, a writing and understanding occasion, for unlocking that vast trunk of images.

This viewing took several weeks of evenings, each session only a couple of hours long, but the total far exceeding the nine hours of my previous marathon, the one that had provided me with the questions I now thought I needed to ask of my father's photographs: What rhetoric would their occasions disclose? Where would my father be found in them? What record of lament and promise would I discover in his narrative of the family history?

These questions can be dealt with quite briefly. A little explanation of the background to the album is necessary, however. My parents brought up my twin brother and myself in the small town of Blenheim. It was a household that had emerged with some difficulty from the Depression – particularly on my mother's side, supported by my resourceful grandmother; on my father's side, there was education: his father was a teacher, and became the principal of the local primary school.

You might say, then, that our family was more than usually driven by the twin goads of fifties 'prosperity': on my mother's side, a powerful urge to escape the traps of hard times – an urge, even, to gentility; on my father's, an urge or even a requirement to live up to the liberating promise of education.

Neither was easy to achieve. 'Progress' was interrupted by the War. Both my parents longed to 'escape'. This might already seem a familiar if thwarted recasting of the rhetoric of prosperity narrated above. So might the solution to my parents' frustration: In 1956, after a brief conspiracy, they took my brother and me and fled, leaving behind all other relatives, dependants, and friends, among whom there would over the years develop a consensus of denunciation strong enough to repel any attempts to 'return', had that ever been likely except at the most formal level.

This was because my parents did not just follow the rhetorical track of prosperity: they went to a remote area of what was then East Pakistan, now Bangladesh, where my father took a job organising the finances of a paper mill a day's journey by river-boat up the Karnafuli river from the port of Chittagong.

248

This rupture, and my parents' subsequent restless relocations, were regarded 'back home' as sufficiently bizarre to constitute a betrayal of the rhetoric of prosperity: they had gone, literally, too far. Their roaming life, and eventually their (to the family 'at home') notorious abandonment of their children, placed them outside the zone of credible progress. Their photographs of exotic locations – especially their photographs of *themselves in* exotic locations – were an affront, indeed a counter-rhetoric; a counter-rhetoric of spendthrift excess rather than earned surplus, of shiftlessness rather than mobility, of snobbishness (or class betrayal) rather than improvement.

The fact that my parents undertook such a bizarre decamping as their first was bad enough. What was worse was that after four years in the jungle (years I remember with extreme pleasure) they meandered enjoyably to Europe where my brother and myself were sent to school in England, while my parents moved on to the next of a long succession of foreign locations, from Pakistan again, to Korea, to Egypt, Jordan, Zambia (then), and so on, with endless excursions about the continents in which they were living.

They retired (twice) to a house in Auckland; the first attempt to 'stay put' was a failure; the second inaugurated what should have been the equivalent of the taxi-driver's elegy, but was not. There was little or no tribute at the end: they had spent their lives and their prosperity.

But how do I know this? Specifically, can I know this from the thousands of photographs my father took? Or can I only read back into those photographs what I already know from the accumulated rumour of family history? Where do I discover a rhetoric that will unite that rumour and those images; and a loop that will declare the complicity of that rhetoric with a larger, let's say sociological, one?

The answer *does* lie in the images: there is a tragic formality in their chaotic progress. This design, as I've said, is not one I would have guessed at, given the experience of my 'understanding' of the taxi-driver's elegy.

My father began to take colour slides from the moment we left New Zealand. To begin with, there is a triumphant tone: the family (minus my father) posed for arrivals and departures at various stages of the adventure.

This foreground, reserved at first for the ceremonial family group, is soon allocated to the exotic: elephants, monuments, river-boats silhouetted before astonishing tropical sunsets, profuse flowers, dead snakes held aloft by children – the foreground is still close, and usually claimed by some combination of my mother and us kids; but that foreground has begun to tear free of the family subject: a subtle transformation of subject into object has begun to take place.

I can next see this process under way through a vast store of images in which family members, increasingly (and eventually only) my mother, are posed near outstanding monuments: temples, cathedrals, works of public art, exotic or famous landmarks such as the Himalayas, the Leaning Tower of Pisa, the Taj Mahal, Michelangelo's *David*, the 'red city' of Petra. At first, the rhetoric is of 'proof': we were here. But increasingly, the sign of family subject is removed. And increasingly, the foreground is left vacant in favour of a middle ground whose object may still be a monument, but whose rhetorical direction has been entirely reversed.

And by degrees, this rhetorical objectification, this jettisoning of fore-grounded family subject, moves its point of focus further and further back. The monuments, wild animals, and other wonders steadily recede: there are tumbled pillars of ruins in Asia Minor, game-park antelopes, dhows at anchor, all beginning to retreat into a mist normally reserved for background. There begin to be landscapes with no obvious salient in them: 'views' that are all background, entirely enigmatic, subjectless (apparently), seemingly also without any object beyond the record itself of purposeless visuality, of an entirely unmediated rhetoric.

If I am to understand that this is a record of the *how* of my father's seeing – that these images literally reproduce how he went on looking at the world he wished to record – then I have to conclude that what he wished to see moved progressively further away from him. Or, to put it another way, that he wished less and less to see what was near at hand. Or, to put the same proposition less emotionally, he was less and less able to see what was close to him.

The rhetoric I discover, then, is less one that unites my father's record with the wider codes of society (as was the case with the taxi-driver's record), as one that progressively removes him from those codes. Watching his slides, I was watching him become absent from the world.

And what of that other absence, the one signalled by his persistence behind the viewfinder? How do I measure the 'unaccountable direction' of his world-view? The paradox is that, just as his progressive absenteeism from looking reverses the direction of the rhetoric discovered in the taxi-driver's slides, so does his 'absence' as object in the world reverse the process discovered above. The more of my father's images I viewed, the more I noticed his retreat from looking, or at least from *noticing*; the more I sought the effects of his absence, by that much more he began to invade the consciousness of the images.

I became more and more aware that it had been *his* eye that had viewed

. . . *this*. Thousands upon thousands of times, he compounded his presence in these images from which his will to see was disappearing. And the more remote, vague, enigmatic, and purposeless these 'views' became, the more I felt his presence. By the end, in some misty valleys with remote peaks, I felt myself almost behind some cataracted consciousness that had been his: behind his very eye, no longer even committed to seeing. His presence in these slides exceeded anything I had experienced of him since early childhood.

And the third term, the elegy? In effect, none whatsoever. Because these images had not accumulated in any way; they had, rather, resulted in a dispersal. Nothing had been overmantled, replaced, improved upon. Appetite had steadily leached from the images. There was, finally, none of the sharpness, none of the focus, none of the possessiveness, of either memory or desire. There was only a vacancy of seeing, a will-less perception, a mere habit, in which my father's presence was inescapably inscribed.

3.

As I come now to write this final episode, I find myself wondering if I might be offending the dead.

I had hoped, by this stage, to have understood why I wanted to write about the album; to have discovered a rhetorical aid to turning its pages; and, prepared by a good reading of research into the album, to have been confident about approaching a single image.

Instead, I find myself quailing before a photograph of my mother that has haunted me for years. When I attempt to unpack this image, it resists everything I think I have learned so far. Instead, it offers a simple warning not found in essays on photography, on photography's etiology and consequences, its sociology, its part in the production of culture. The warning: Respect the dead.

This, photography does not do. How could it? Photography is only the record of light meeting chemically prepared paper. It does not 'respect' (or disrespect) anything. This the photographer may do (as was the case with the taxi-driver's memorial). But if we have lost any record of or connection with the photographer, how are we to judge the respect (or otherwise) of light's action upon film?

Usually, the album allows us to take for granted some measure of affection or respect in the recordist, even where these terms are made strange, as in the case of my own father's album. And the images of the portfolio, of the gallery, are usually endorsed by sufficient discourse for us to be able to reconstruct at least something of the photograph's record of intention.

251

But the image of my mother that I am looking at is ambiguously unmediated in this respect. It belongs in an album. Equally, it is a 'studio' photograph. It preserves intact a fragment of memory; at the same time it poses an entirely artificial moment.

It is a black-and-white tableau of an incident in a production of *The Admirable Crichton* by the Blenheim Operatic Society some time before World War II. I know it was before the War, because the cast includes three men who wouldn't be there later, and because my mother is still very young: in her early twenties, one might guess.

This is an album photograph because it records a domestic and family-history fact, namely that my mother was a passionate player in operettas and repertory productions in Blenheim. To that extent it is not 'posed' at all, and it is quite respectful of my mother's memory.

It is also, however, and perhaps primarily, an entirely posed production shot, with the amateur cast rather stiffly holding attitudes, dressed in animal skins, a monocle, and so forth; as such, given that the recordist is unambiguously 'absent' in a way the album photographer can never be (even allowing for such different kinds of absence as those of the taxi-driver, and of my father), the issue of respect or otherwise is simply withheld.

Approaching this photograph, then – approaching this bizarrely posed image of my mother as a beautiful young woman – I find myself approaching an ambiguity or even a complicity between respect and indifference, between affection and chemical reaction to light, that I can find no way of reconciling.

This complicity implicates the photograph's propositions of my mother as 'posed' and as 'young'. How am I to resist this conflation of her youth with her pose? How to resist the implication that her youth *is* a pose? That her *glamour*, even, no less than her animal skins and leafy chaplet, is artificial; *that her life itself is theatrical?*

This thought alarms and saddens me, especially since my last memory of my mother is of her difficult death. On the other hand, we may be offered a liberation here. This complicity of theatre with memory, of the rhetorical with the domestic, of indifference with respect, allows us to utter one in terms of the other. It confounds the distinction between the emotional album and the impersonal machinery of photography – a distinction still upheld in different ways by the albums of the taxi-driver and of my father.

With respect, then – what do I see? I see six amateur actors dressed in clumsy prop skins (my mother's are dashing deer skins). They are heavy-handedly posed in two groups of three: in each group, two are standing while one is down on one knee. The two groups are divided by the bow held by my mother. All are gazing in alarm at something concealed beyond the left side of the frame (my mother's expression is more amused than anything else). One wears a wrist-watch and glasses, another a monocle (my mother wears an elegant chaplet of 'leaves', and she has the best shoes).

I am already beginning to favour her (as an album would). But in fact 'the photograph' (which is to say the record) itself does so as well. She is clearly the central figure: she bends a bow and aims an arrow at the unseen presence stage-right; a quiver of elaborately feathered shafts is slung over her left shoulder; she is the central action figure and the rest of the players are directed by her pose – they are in reaction to her presence.

What do I see? I see my beautiful young mother. I see her at the centre of events. I see that she is not afraid. I see that she is more stylish than the rest.

What do I see? My beautiful young mother as a Diana/Artemis huntress figure, bending her bow. Her epithets include the founding of towns and the protection of young animals.

What do I see? My beautiful young mother who would protect her children, bending her bow against an unseen enemy.

Bending her bow at, repulsing, that unseen directorial presence, that author, that point of view, that will tell her how to live and how to appear, that will pose her as accessory, that will make her life theatrical: call it 'society', this invisible tyrant, which sociology might generalise from an individual ambition.

On her forearm bracing the bow, I already see the bone bracelet which, as a child, I would beg her to take off because I was afraid of the thought that it would be on her when she died. She did take it off and never wore it again. It was not on her when she died. Perhaps sixty years after the photograph was taken, I keep the bracelet and the picture of it together in the same drawer.

4.

This inconclusion I have come to (a memento in the drawer of a middle-aged man) in respect of the family album, seems to have been arrived at by four stages, between which conflicts fall like sudden alterations of perspective, focus or lighting, anomalous and immoderate.

Firstly, by the idea that the family album is simultaneously the record of a public rhetoric. Secondly, by the idea that the invisibility of the recordist can be, finally, all the record contains. Thirdly, that the distinction between emotion and process may not be sustainable. Fourthly, that photographs themselves may resist the idea that they merely mythologise the record. What we may discover, in the end, is that they resist intention (and even respect for the dead) in order to occupy a space equivalent to, the equal of, commensurate with, their subjects. Moving beyond metonymy into something like alchemy, the stand-for images of the family album become as weighty as what they once merely represented. The emotion we feel in their presence is not quite vicarious. The only father I have is in a trunkful of images of receding horizons. The only mother I have lives in a theatrical photograph alongside the bracelet she removed because her child feared it as a presage of death. These images are souls. The album is their reliquary. I am not by nature superstitious, but I have learned this.

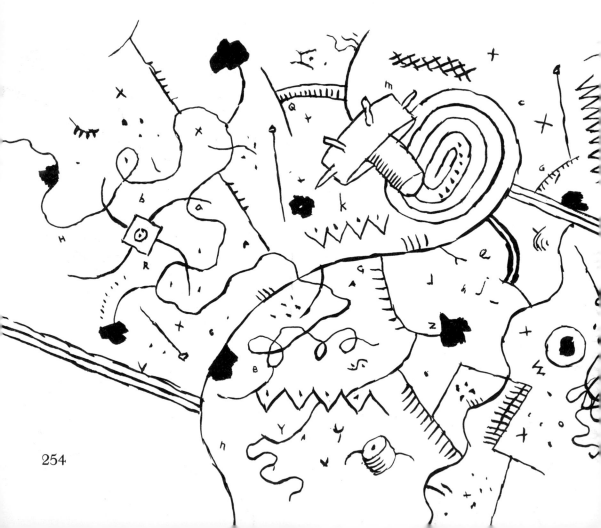

EAVAN BOLAND
Lava Cameo

I like this story –
My grandfather was a sea-captain.
My grandmother always met him when his ship docked.
She feared the women at the ports –

except that it is not a story,
more a rumour or a folk-memory,
something thrown out once in a random conversation;
a hint merely.

If I say wool and lace for her skirt and
crêpe for her blouse
in the neck of which is pinned a cameo,
carved out of black, volcanic rock;

if I make her pace the Cork docks, stopping
to take down her parasol as a gust catches
the silk tassels of it, then
consider this:

There is a way of making free with the past,
a pastiche of what is
real and what is
not, which can only be

justified if you think of it
not as sculpture but syntax:
a structure extrinsic to meaning which uncovers
the inner secret of it.

She will die at twenty-eight in a fever ward.
He will drown nine years later in the Bay of Biscay.
They will never even be
sepia and so I put down

the gangplank now between the ship and the ground.
In the story, late afternoon has become evening.
They kiss once. Their hands touch briefly.
Please,

look at me, I want to say to her: show me
the obduracy of an art which can
arrest a profile in the flux of hell.
Inscribe catastrophe.

MICHAEL CARSON
On the Left Side

Anyone who visits St Finbar's during Sunday Mass will be fascinated by the queer seating arrangements. The right side of the church is filled to bursting, while only ten people – myself and nine other sinners – sit on the left.

It's a huge church, St Finbar's, built during the Troubles by rebellious Canon O'Rourke to cock a snook at the Church of Ireland pile near by. And in those early days it was filled to bursting every Sunday. But the population of Conn, County Mayo, has decreased since – we Irish, I often think, are bred just for export – and the pews are only half filled most weeks. In the sixties a rich farmer left the church some money in his will on condition that it was spent on providing some heat for the church, a draughty place even in summer and enough to turn the Pope protestant in winter. Father O'Rourke, the great nephew of the church's builder, reluctantly shelled out on enough electric wall-heaters to heat half the church. The right half. The left was left as it had been and was used not at all, except by the odd mad tourist. The whole congregation made a beeline for the right side . . . until, that is, Sister Philomena O'Halloran sent us her Christmas present.

We in Conn have always prided ourselves on our missionary activity. Rows of competing missionary boxes have lined the counter at Hephernan's grocer's ever since I was a girl. Old man Hephernan would dish out the change in tiny denominations and would take a very dim view of anyone who left his shop without making the missionary boxes clink. Failure to contribute had been known to cut the miser's credit to the bone. At school we saved black babies by the gross, cured lepers past computation. Most of us had never been further than Castlebar but our influence – or so we were taught – spread itself far and wide across the heathen world.

So we were all very excited when Father O'Rourke announced that the other half of the farmer's money was to be spent on a very special charity. Conn was to send one of its daughters to Burundi to set up and run a medical mission. The town was agog, wondering who would be chosen. There were a lot to choose from. Conn produced nuns and nurses and combinations of the two as other towns produce, say, tweed or tea cosies. At last news reached us that Philomena O'Halloran of the Poor Sisters of St Thaddeus had been chosen.

Philomena O'Halloran, a small nun with twinkling blue eyes and the

O'Hallorans' prominent chin, was given a special Mass and breakfast before being seen off on the Dublin train. The missionary boxes disappeared overnight from pub, shop and church door to be replaced by one, the Sister Philomena fund. And Mr Hephernan began saying as he handed people their change, 'Here's your Philomena money.'

To his credit he never stopped saying it, though a few years later a supermarket opened on the outskirts of the town robbing him of much custom. Ireland joined the common market and poor farmers discarded their donkeys and bought Austin Eleven Hundreds, left thatched cottages to rot and built white bungalows. Irish towns began to be twinned with unpronounceable places on the continent whose people came to visit us and bought the discarded cottages of the newly rich farmers. Conn, however, was twinned with Obtu, Burundi, where Sister Philomena continued to fight the good fight out of sight, but never quite out of mind.

We heard news of our African apostolate seated on the right side of St Finbar's each Sunday. Father O'Rourke read us letters from Philomena O'Halloran and held special collections more often than some thought was called for, saying that he wanted to hear the rustle of notes rather than the jingling of change. A noticeboard at the back of the church showed us pictures of what was being wrought in the African forests. We saw row upon row of smiling African children, Sister Philomena injecting black arms, comforting the old and the lame. She had discarded her navy-blue habit for a blouse and a pair of shorts — something which raised the eyebrows of a number of conservatives — but there was no denying that much was being achieved.

Conn had been supporting the Sister Philomena mission for over two decades when Sister Philomena wrote that she was going to send us a Christmas present in the form of a young man from the mission. The young man's father, she said, would pay the fare but it would be appreciated if accommodation could be offered. I offered, but so did everybody else and in the end the Widow Hephernan was chosen. The Widow Hephernan lived alone (Grocer Hephernan having passed on to his reward in 1981) in a large house. To provide hospitality to a real live African was seen as the pinnacle of achievement. And this African had been brought up by our own special saint.

A group of Conn notables was waiting on the station for the arrival of the Dublin train. I watched from a distance, eating a Crunchie by the ticket window and making eyes at Declan Lyons the station master, who's far too nice to be a bachelor. The train arrived a few minutes early, for a change. I should have known then that momentous events were in the wind. A full minute passed, during which time I finished my Crunchie and wondered whether I should go off and spread the news that the African had failed to arrive. But had I done that I would have opened myself to castigation from the pulpit on the Sunday following for, just as my legs ached to hoof off to O'Flaherty's, a small figure appeared at the far end of the platform, holding a brown suitcase. He looked up the platform towards the group and then started walking towards it.

As the young man approached I saw Father O'Rourke's jaw drop, quickly followed by those of the rest of the group. I could not at first see what had caused their surprise but when the lad came closer I dropped my Crunchie wrapper, and had not Declan Lyons drawn attention to my lapse I do not think I would have noticed.

The sight of the young African was a shock. He was lighter than most Africans, a beautiful creamed coffee colour. It was his face, though, which caused the jaws of Conn to drop and in the days that followed got them wagging. For the African had cornflower-blue eyes and the O'Halloran chin.

'Hello,' he said. 'My name's Friday Mkete. I have come to spend Christmas with my benefactors.'

'What sort of name is Friday for a Christian?' asked Father O'Rourke, looking suspicious.

Now I, being a simple sort of girl, who has read her Tarzan books to Leaving Certificate level, would have thought the answer to that was obviously that Friday was called Friday because he had been born on a Friday. Friday, however, surprised us.

'My father is called Thursday.'

That appealed to me greatly. What everybody with the least acquaintance with the O'Halloran physiognomy – just about everyone with eyes – wanted to know was what had Thursday done to Sister Philomena? It seemed as clear as the chin on your face that it was something which had dawned as Friday. And, if our presentiments were true, what on earth had got into Philomena to let her sin find her out after all those years?

The thing was that nobody had the courage to ask the question. I think, in those days before Christmas, had anyone plucked up the required puff to climb Ben Brandon – the mountain that broods over Conn – and look back down at the town at his feet he would have seen written above it as if in sky-writing: IS PHILOMENA O'HALLORAN YOUR MOTHER? Nobody did, of course. I remember when Friday's picture appeared on the front of the *Conn Advertiser* seeing the Widow Hephernan poring over the picture and comparing the likeness to that of Sister Philomena on the front of the mission box. When the Widow Hephernan saw me seeing her she stood up straight and asked me what she could do for me in a way that betokened that if she had her way nothing further could or would be done for me, seeing as I was a fallen woman. Still I'm used to such looks. I've been fallen long enough – down so long it seems like up to me, as the unwilling emigrants that share Friday's blood might say.

In the event, though, the question did not need to be asked because Friday told us without the least prompting. He had been taken on a pilgrimage down to O'Flaherty's bar by some buckos who had been feeling that it must be miserable for a poor African to be at the Widow Hephernan's, forced to eat pilchard sandwiches with the crusts cut off, drink gallons of tea and kneel down to the rosary as soon as Telefis Erin was off the air. The buckos took no notice of Widow Hephernan's looks, even though it would probably send their credit rating at Hephernan's grocer's to the devil. Friday downed a pint of Guinness faster than a monsignor, or a bookie on his way back from Kildare, remarking that it was not as strong as African beer. Then he said, as bold as brass, that his mum made the best hooch south of the Tanzan railroad – whatever that is when it's at home.

'Tell us about your mum, Friday.'

And Friday did.

This happened on the night before Christmas Eve, so the news of Sister Philomena's disgrace had a full day to spread around Conn before Christmas Mass.

The right side of the church was packed out when Friday came in alone. The Widow Hephernan had obviously decided that the shame was too great for her to put in an appearance. He walked down the aisle with every eye in the place on him. He did not seem at all concerned, but took his seat in the very front row on the left.

Mass began and I swear that nobody in the church was paying the least attention to the goings on on the altar. All eyes were glued to the single brown man on the left side of the church. When the time came for the sermon Father O'Rourke mounted the steps of the pulpit with a face of thunder and launched into a sermon about the Last Judgement – one we would expect to hear at the start of Lent rather than on the day of our Saviour's birth. He talked of the good on the right of God and the wicked on the left. He talked of whited sepulchres and sins against holy purity and the torment meted out to hypocrites.

I sat there going hot and cold with a mixture of anger, embarrassment and fear. It was as clear as the nose on your face that Father O'Rourke was addressing Philomena O'Halloran sitting there in front of him in the form of Friday Mkete. I had received similar treatment when I told Father O'Rourke about my baby – though mercifully in the little cubby hole of confession. But the public humiliation being meted out to this innocent lad made me angry in a way I had never been angry before. I wanted to stand up and protest. Then I thought I should walk out and never darken the doors of St Finbar's again. But I sat. Father O'Rourke kept on and on about the sheep on the right and the goats on the left and suddenly a strange thing happened. Simultaneously a few of the congregation stood up, pushed their way to the centre aisle, genuflected and went and sat on Friday's side of the church. It took me a while to realise what was happening but when I did I went and joined them. Friday had not even looked round. I am not sure to this day whether he was aware of what was happening.

That might have been enough but it didn't end there. Father O'Rourke – truly a man with all the finesse of a Mullingar heifer – finished his hellfire sermon, making no mention of Christmas or the special collection for Burundi, and returned to the altar. Then, during the offertory I saw Miss Dwyer, who is Father O'Rourke's housekeeper and in charge of St Finbar's crib, leave her place on the right and disappear into the sacristy. She emerged a minute later with a statue of one of the Three Kings – the black one – and trundled it across the front of the church, though it was almost as big as herself and must have weighed as much as a sack of spuds. Behind the curtain covering the crib until after Mass she went, every eye in the place, including Father O'Rourke's, on her. There were some sounds of scraping and back she came and sat herself down next to me – slipping me a merry wink – in good time for the consecration.

Father O'Rourke elevated the Host, his hands shaking visibly, and we all – on right and left – bowed our heads as we had been taught. I said a prayer for Philomena O'Halloran in the middle of her twentieth Christmas away from home but with her felix culpa, her greatest achievement, kneeling in front of us.

After Mass Father O'Rourke asked Miss Dwyer why she had placed one of the Three Kings in the crib when they are not supposed to arrive until the Epiphany.

'Sure, didn't this one arrive early?' she replied.

Well, Friday Mkete returned to Africa many Guinnesses later. Miss Dwyer still keeps house for Father O'Rourke, though he no longer has special collections for the Philomena mission. The Widow Hephernan has removed her box from the counter of her shop. Those of us who sat on the left side of the church that Christmas Eve still do, and we do our best to collect money among the sinners and publicans of County Mayo. What we are able to send to Philomena is not as much as before but she seems to be managing. Still, it's a bit cold over here on the left of the church, away from the heat and the good sheep. We just wrap up warm and try to keep cheerful.

And usually we do, thank God.

GREGORY O'BRIEN
Two Poems

A Recipe for Custard

These are the things
that keep us together:
the blue mountains

a musician dozing
against the elephant
tree, clarinet

embedded in blue soil.
Morning reaches this
far, touches evening

the Hydro Majestic
a palace overthrown
by leaves. Nights

made of canvas, stretched
to any length and held
there, bath-water golden

from the clay reservoir.
We dream an orchestra
asleep outside

on the tennis courts
hear the concrete dolphin
swim across an ancient

pool, and wonder if the
cable-car will reach
the Three Sisters,

how far these mountains reach
down into the ground.
By morning the orchestra

will be out of work,
the ballroom will resume
its emptiness

another year. And
the musicians will hide
the concrete dolphin in

the back of a van which
by late afternoon
will have reached

the coast. We will
follow in the evening
find them on a beach

gathering kelp
they will take home
and share as custard.

New Place

You lie on a bed with three long
thin cats

one white, one ginger, one black
the long brushes

of their tails. While nine thousand miles
away

Philip Guston lies with three
tubes of paint

— white, cadmium red, black —
and three

brushes beside him
in his grave.

GERALD MURNANE

Some Books Are to be Dropped into Wells, Others into Fishponds . . .

The other day I stood in front of my bookshelves and stared at the spine of *Don Quixote*. According to my meticulously kept records I read that book in 1970, but when I stood staring at its spine I could remember nothing of the book itself or of the experience of reading it. I could remember no phrase, no sentence; I could not remember one moment from all the hours when I had sat with that bulky book open in front of me.

After I had waited in vain for some words from the book to come back to me, I kept a lookout for images. I waited to see some flickering scenes in black and white on the invisible screen that hangs about a metre in front of my eyes wherever I go. But not even the ghost of a scene appeared from the book. For a moment I thought I saw a silhouette of a man on horseback, but then I recognised it as a memory of the print of Daumier's painting of Don Quixote that had hung on the wall in front of where I stood until I had had extra bookshelves built there.

I gave up waiting for *Don Quixote* and performed the same test on other books. From a sample of twelve – all of them read before 1976 and never opened since – I found seven that brought nothing to mind. If this was a fair sample, then of all the books that I had read once and had not read again, more than half had been wholly forgotten within a few years. I wondered whether I was entitled to conclude that the forgotten books had been of no use to me. I wondered whether I might have better promoted my health and happiness by going for walks or doing push-ups or taking naps instead of reading those books that were going to fly away so soon from my mind. I wondered whether I might as conveniently have dropped those books down a well as read them. (Yet how could I have known at the time which books I ought to read and which books make a splash with?)

I could still not believe that so many books had left so little trace behind them. I decided that my memories of them must be buried deep. I decided to poke around in the dark places – the back rooms of my mind. I closed my eyes and said aloud over and over, '*Don Quixote*, by Miguel de Cervantes, is one of the greatest works of fiction of any age.'

While repeating these solemn words I remembered an evening in 1967 when I was a part-time student at the University of Melbourne. A lecturer in English, during a lecture on *Tom Jones*, read out in class a passage from *Don Quixote*. No doubt the lecturer was making a very important point, but I have forgotten the point today. All I remember is that the passage quoted from Cervantes was concerned with a person or persons (I think they may have been aboard a ship) being struck in the face by a quantity of wind-borne human vomit.

This seemed an odd memory to have been connected with a great work of fiction, but it was the only result of my reciting the mantra about the book. If anyone reading this has a detailed knowledge of *Don Quixote* and has never read in the great book a passage about wind-borne vomit, that person need not trouble to correct me on the point. I am not writing about *Don Quixote* but about my memory of the books on my shelves.

And now I remember one more result of my repeating aloud the words in praise of *Don Quixote*. As I said the words aloud, I became convinced that I had said them on at least one previous occasion – and not to myself, as I happened to be saying the words then, but in company. In short, I became aware that I was a person who sometimes delivered ponderous judgements on books without being able to remember any more than the name of the book, the author's name, and some judgement borrowed from someone else. This awareness made me embarrassed. I remembered people who had agreed with me when I had uttered my judgements – and people who had disagreed. I might have felt urged to seek out those people and to apologise to them. But what saved me from doing this was a suspicion that some at least of the people who had discussed the great books with me might have remembered no more about the books than I did.

Within a few days I had learned to accept myself as a man who could remember absolutely nothing about *Don Quixote* except the name of the author. I even dared to suppose the abyss in my memory might be a sort of distinction. Even the most forgetful among my friends would surely remember one passage at least from *Don Quixote*, but there I was with my memory a perfect blank. I remembered that Jorge Luis Borges had written a story with the title 'Pierre Menard, Author of the *Quixote*'. Even Borges, with his fertile imagination, could imagine nothing stranger than that a man of our time could *write* the whole of *Don Quixote*; even Borges could never have supposed that a seemingly literate and civilised man could read and then *forget* the whole of the immortal work.

I became interested in the question why I remembered certain books and forgot others. I must emphasise, however, that the books I am writing about are books I have not looked into for at least fifteen years. On my shelves are many books that I read or look into every few years, and some books that I have to pick up and look into whenever I catch sight of them. My memory of these books too is strangely uneven, but for the moment I am writing about the long-forgotten and the long-remembered.

Some books that I have not read for more than thirty years have left me with images that I see nearly every day. The images are by no means comforting. I can never quite believe those people who write as adults about the joys and pleasures of their childhood reading. As a child I was made restless and unhappy by most of the books that I read. Whether the book was meant to have a happy or unhappy ending, I was always distressed by the mere fact that the book had an ending. After reading a book I would go into the backyard and try to build a model of the landscape where the characters in the book had lived, and where they could go on living under my supervision and encouragement. Or I tried to draw maps of their houses or farms or districts, or to write in secret in the backs of old exercise books an endless continuation of the book that I had wanted not to end. Often I included myself among the characters in these prolongations.

The first book that I remember as affecting me in this way is *Man-Shy*, by Frank Dalby Davison. I first read *Man-Shy* when I was eight. I read it again soon afterwards, but I cannot remember having read it since and I could not say when I last looked between the covers of the book. What I am writing today about *Man-Shy* comes from memory; I am writing about images that have stayed with me for most of my life.

I remember the red cow. As I remember her now, the red cow stands on a hilltop in Queensland in a year not long before I was born. (My father had told me that the book was set in Queensland in the 1930s.) Probably no week of my life has passed without my seeing for a moment the red cow as she appeared in the little line-drawing beneath the last lines of the text of my father's red-covered Angus and Robertson edition. I have never been to Queensland; I have never ridden a horse or seen a sheep being shorn; yet I have remembered all my life an image of a red cow on a hill in outback Queensland.

The red cow is dying of thirst. I am not going to check the text after all these years. I will quote what I have always remembered as the last words of the text: 'She was about to join the shadowy herd that had gone from the ranges for ever.'

Even while I typed these words just now, I felt the same painful uncertainty that I used to feel as a child. Was the red cow actual or imaginary? If the cow was actual I could at least be sure that her suffering was over. But in that case I could no longer hope that the cow I had read about would miraculously survive.

If the cow was imagined, then I wanted to ask the author what would happen to her in his imagination. Would she finally die like an actual cow? Or had the author found a way of thinking of her as alive in spite of everything?

The red cow and her calf were dying because their last waterhole had been fenced around. They were the last survivors in the wild of a herd that had been driven in from the bush to a cattle station. The owners of the station had fenced the waterholes, and the red cow and her calf were about to die from thirst.

By the age of eight I had been thoroughly taught in the eschatology of the Catholic Church. Yet nothing I had been taught could help me decide what would happen to the red cow if she died – or what *had* happened to the cow if she had already died. I knew without asking that animals lacked souls. For an animal there was no heaven or hell, only the earth. But I could not bear to think of the red cow as living on earth and then dying for ever. I clung to the words on the last page . . . the red cow was going to join the shadowy herd.

I laid out in my backyard a vast savanna for that shadowy herd. I studded the savanna with waterholes. I reduced myself in size like Dollman in the comic book. ('By a supreme effort of the will he compresses the molecules of his body and becomes . . . Dollman!') I led my shadowy herd to the waterholes and watched them drink. I stood beside the red cow while she drank unafraid from the pool at my feet.

Sometimes I left my shadowy herd in a valley while I climbed a hill to look around me. If I saw far away towards the east the cleared land and the ocean, I could still turn towards the west and see my savanna reaching far inland.

If the red cow had not been dying of thirst, she would have seen from the hill where she stood at the end of the book the edge of the blue Pacific Ocean. In that scene the blue smudge of the ocean has no other purpose than to mark the far edge of the land where the red cow has been driven to her death. For most of my life the ocean has been no more to me than a boundary marker.

Today while I think of the ocean to the east of the red cow, I am reminded of *Moby-Dick*.

I have not looked between the covers of *Moby-Dick* for nineteen years but I remember rather more of the book than I remember of *Don Quixote*. This need not tell against *Don Quixote*, which I read only for pleasure whereas *Moby-Dick* was one of my set texts for English at university – in the same year, as it happens, when I heard about the flying vomit in Cervantes. In 1967 I read the whole of *Moby-Dick* twice through with care and some chapters more than twice.

Yet even so, *Moby-Dick* has lasted well in my mind by comparison with other set texts from the same years. I can recall without effort today two sentences (one of them is the first sentence, of course), a phrase of three words, and some of the images that occurred to me while I read the text twenty years ago. I can recall also the conviction that I had while I read. I was convinced that the narrator of *Moby-Dick* was the wisest and most engaging narrator I had met in fiction.

The image that comes to me from *Moby-Dick* today is of a toy-like ship on a smooth, green expanse of water. The ship is not a whaling vessel but the sixteenth-century Portuguese caravel that I copied in grade seven into my history notebook from a line-drawing in a textbook. On the tiny deck of the toy boat two men stand talking. A few vague figures of other men hang like monkeys in the rigging, but they are there only for decoration – none of them actually does anything. The reason for this is that all my life I have skipped over the technical terms and descriptions in all the books I have read about ships and boats; I have never understood the difference between a bosun and a capstan.

I have only just noticed that the deck of the toy ship is dotted with pots of the same shape and proportions as the pots in which cartoon cannibals cook cartoon missionaries and pith-helmeted explorers. And now, when I look again at the smooth, green water around the toy boat, I am looking not at the Pacific Ocean but at the surface of what might be a kiddies' wading pool. I can see from New Zealand to South America in one glance.

The pots are simmering on the deck because I remember having read in *Moby-Dick* that the oil from the catch of the whales was boiled and purified on deck when the sea was especially calm and the weather fine. I could hardly have read that the crew kept a supply of cartoon cooking-pots for this purpose, and now that I have begun this sentence I remember that the fires for heating the boiling-vessels burned in ovens made of brick. The bricks for the ovens, I have just remembered, were laid with mortar on the deck and were afterwards broken apart when they had served their purpose.

Why have I remembered just now the brick ovens on the toy ship, when for the past twenty years I thought of them as cartoon cooking-pots?

In January 1987 I was halfway through writing what would be my fifth book of fiction. At the time I was not writing well. When I recognise that I am not writing well, I suppose I am staring too hard at what lies in front of my face. I try to stop staring and to notice what lies at the edges of my view. In January 1987 I had been staring for too long at soil. I was writing about a character who was staring at the soil of his native district in order to understand why he always felt drawn to that district. But then I sat back a little and noticed what was at the edge of my view. I noticed a fishpond.

The pond was not one of those bean-shaped ornamental pools overhung with ferns and pampas grass. It was a plain-looking square of bricks rising abruptly from the back lawn behind a house where I had lived for two years as a boy. As soon as I had noticed this pond at the edge of my view I knew I had found the image that would keep me writing until my book was finished. I felt as though I only had to stare at the brick walls rising out of the grass, or at the little grub-shaped bits of dried mortar still sticking between the bricks, or at the dark-green water with the raft of floating water-plants whose leaves were like shamrocks – I only had to stare at these things and all the rest of the story I had been trying for three years to tell would appear to me.

It was a strange experience to discover, halfway through writing what I thought was a story about X, that I had really been writing the story of Y. I had thought for three years that I was writing a book whose central image was a patch of soil and grass, but one day in January 1987 I learned that the central image of my book was a fishpond.

It was also a strange experience to discover that I remembered after twenty years the brick ovens on the deck, and to see the ovens as having the shape and size of the fishpond that had recently yielded half a book of fiction. The American poet Robert Bly once wrote that he learned to be a poet when he learned to trust his obsessions. I trusted my image of the fishpond and found in the image of the pond what I needed for finishing my story. I thought when I had finished the story that I had finished with the pond. I had even written into the last part of the story a description of the pond as empty of water and of the red fish that had lived in the pond as drowning in air. But now an image of the same fishpond has appeared on the deck of the *Pequod* – or, rather, many images of fishponds have appeared on deck; and all the fishponds are bubbling like stewpots.

Before I look into the bubbling ponds, I ask myself how I could have lived for more than thirty years without realising how full of meaning my fishpond was. I had never forgotten the pond; I would have thought of my own pond whenever I saw a pond in someone's lawn. But I had not understood how much of meaning was contained in the pond. I was given a hint sometimes, but I failed to follow it up. During most of the thirty-five years after I had left the house with the fishpond on the back lawn, I would become oddly alert whenever I noticed in a front garden a certain small variety of begonia with glossy red and green leaves. I always supposed the leaves themselves would one day remind me of something important; but I was staring at what was in front of me when I should have been watching out for things at the edge of my vision. In the house where I had lived in 1950 and 1951, a row of begonias had grown along the side fence. If I had stood and stared at those begonias I would have seen the pond from the corner of my eye.

The connection between my fishpond of 1951 and the bubbling pots on the deck of the *Pequod* is not only that the pond and the fireplaces were both of brick. The pond and the boiling oil are connected by the fact that the bricks on the deck were laid especially for the purpose and later removed.

Two years after my family had moved from the house with the fishpond, a tradesman left behind in the backyard of the house where we then lived a small heap of bricks and some unused wet mortar. While the mortar was still wet I decided I would build a small fishpond on the lawn. I wanted to have green water-plants and chubby red fish in my backyard again. But after I had assembled the first row of bricks for my pond, my father ordered me to stop.

The boiling that took place in the fishponds on the *Pequod* was for the purpose of refining the substance that the narrator of *Moby-Dick* calls mostly *sperm*.

I wrote earlier that I remembered a sentence apart from the first sentence of *Moby-Dick*. As I have remembered it for twenty years and without consulting the text, the sentence is uttered by Captain Ahab to Mr Starbuck not long before the last chase begins. An unfamiliar smell has been wafted into the noses of the two men. In my memory, Captain Ahab does a turn about the deck in the manner of Long John Silver as drawn in Classic Comics, smells the strange smell, and says, 'They are making hay in the meadows of the Andes, Mr Starbuck.'

I happen to have been born without a sense of smell. I can form no idea of the smell of hay being made. When I remember the words that I put into Captain Ahab's mouth just then, I merely see long grass growing in a place such as I have seen in photographs of the *altiplano* of Bolivia. But because I know there is something about the grassy place that I can never experience, I look at it intently, as though I might be allowed to see more in the grass than a person would see who was able to smell it.

Because I have never experienced the smelling of a thing from a distance, I suppose that a person must always be in sight of what he gets wind of. Whenever I see Ahab and Starbuck with the smell of hay in their noses I see them as in sight of land. The two men stand on the deck of their toy boat. The two are alone by now. I see no other men doing pretend-tasks or hanging idly in the rigging. The sea around the toy boat is smooth and green. I can see from end to end of the green water. The world is smaller by far than I had supposed.

Somewhere in his writings, Robert Musil reminds us of how wrong we are to think of the individual self as the one unstable item within a firm world. The opposite is the case. The unstable world drifts like an island at the heart of each of us.

When I look intently at the ocean around the *Pequod*, the green water is the fishpond. At the edge of my vision I see a grassy hill. The world is a small place by now; Queensland and South America are the one grassy hill above the pond.

The red cow smells the water. She goes down from the meadows of hay towards the pool that keeps her alive.

JOHN ASHBERY
Livelong Days

Feather in your cap? Not from heeding
the half-lit messages of other writers
you cherish and would like to forget.
I sat at my desk; the storm was brewing
on an April morning. The sun still shone
and the bud had blasted. There were shadows on the ground.
Yet I sat, not doing, not worrying whether we're living in it right.
And when her younger sister found out who I was,
why, that would take precedence. Certainly
we'd all be here a while longer
that would mean time to find out,
to test the fiddle's scrolled-up tensions
in case everything came out all right.

Those were the days for living in a sack,
a loose one for answering the door in.
the neighbours kept you up all night
with whispering and indecisions. It was time to
look into *Aunt Agatha's Tried and True Recipes* just to see
who was mulling it and if they could
somehow get back to you once the joint was cold.
Alas, these spoke only in terms appropriate to the occasion,
too much so, in fact. Where was the residue
of calm fear, the notices
to convene with the lawn chairs, that prompted inspection of other
recent ordinances? And the doormat wiggled like a ghost
in the draft under the door but there was quite a lot to be said
and none willing to go down, slog down if need be, the painted stair
whose ends were invisible
in this tide of sick summer light
wherever feet chose to take one, here

among the weeds and provisions, there in the rue,
and make chaff of all we built, all we had constructed against?

That is a way of being, it said. All right,
I won't argue, but show me the increment, fine as lint,
apparently, that tips it, festoons
a tree in the room, and finally delivers the book
to a publisher just as the door is closing? I won't envy it.
If I had the wings of an angel something, or everything,
would be slightly different, and you'd see: it would
come out in play. The differences that make us inexact now would
chase us into learning from that space, that pure longing
for the pauses just past, multiplying like mythologies, apples.

Contributor's Notes

Barbara Anderson is the 1991 Writing Fellow at Victoria University of Wellington. She began writing in her fifties and has published a book of short stories and a novel, *Girls High*.

John Ashbery lives in New York City. He has won many awards for his writing – including the Pulitzer Prize and the National Book Award for *Self-portrait in a Convex Mirror* – and is one of America's most distinguished poets.

Eavan Boland's poetry includes a *Selected Poems* and – most recently – *Outside History* which was a Poetry Book Society Choice in 1990. She lives in Dublin.

Jenny Bornholdt is a New Zealander who has made a single journey overseas. Her books include *This Big Face* and *Moving House*.

Jane Campion lives in Sydney and has been widely acclaimed for her films, which include *Sweetie*, and *An Angel at My Table*, an adaptation of Janet Frame's autobiography.

Michael Carson lives in London. He has written four novels: the bestselling *Sucking Sherbert Lemons*, *Friends and Infidels*, *Coming Up Roses*, and *Stripping Penguins Bare*.

Angela Carter lives in London. Her novel, *Wise Children*, was published earlier this year, and she recently edited the *Virago Book of Fairy-Tales*. An earlier version of 'Ashputtle' appeared in the *VLS*.

Charles Causley lives in Launceston, Cornwall, but travels widely. Last year he received the prestigious Ingersoll/T.S. Eliot Award for his poetry. 'After School' is from 'an unfinished autobiography'.

Robert Crawford lectures at St Andrews University and is a co-editor of the magazine, *Verse*. His poetry collection, *A Scottish Assembly*, was published last year.

Philip Davison lives in Dublin. His fourth novel, The *Makeweight*, will be published in the spring of next year. He also writes television drama.

Simeon Dumdum Jr lives in Cebu City in the Philippines; he writes in his native Cebuano as well as in English. His most recent book of poems is *Third World Opera*.

Jeff Fisher is from Australia. He lives and works in London.

Helen Garner writes film scripts as well as fiction. Her books include *Monkey Grip*, *Postcards from Surfers*, and *The Children's Bach*. She lives in Melbourne.

Jorie Graham is the author of four volumes of poetry, including *The End of Beauty* and *Region of Unlikeness*. She is on the permanent faculty at the University of Iowa, and lives in Iowa City with her husband and daughter.

Bernadette Hall lives in Christchurch, New Zealand, and has recently been Writing Fellow at the University of Canterbury. Her poetry collections are *Heartwood* and *Of Elephants etc.*

Dinah Hawken is a New Zealander whose collection, *It Has No Sound and is Blue*, won the Commonwealth Poetry Prize for best first book in 1987.

Seamus Heaney's new book of poems, *Seeing Things*, was published earlier this year. He is Professor of Poetry at the University of Oxford.

Lauren Holder lives in Auckland. 'We Have Lost a Woman' is her first published work.

Elizabeth Jolley began writing in Australia, after emigrating from the United Kingdom in 1959. Her books include *Woman in a Lampshade*, *Mr Scobie's Riddle*, and *My Father's Moon*. 'My First Editor' is part of a longer memoir which will appear in the Gale's Contemporary Authors Autobiography Series.

Lloyd Jones lives in Eastbourne, New Zealand. He has published two novels, *Gilmore's Dairy* and *Splinter*, and is about to publish a collection of stories.

Elizabeth Knox has written a novel, *After Z-Hour*, and a novella, *Paremata*. She is a co-editor of the New Zealand magazine, *Sport*, where a longer version of her essay appeared.

Joan London works in a bookshop in Fremantle. Her book of stories, *Sister Ships*, won the *Age* Book of the Year Award.

Margaret Mahy lives at Governors Bay, in New Zealand's South Island, in a house she partly built herself. She has twice won the Carnegie Medal for her children's fiction.

Owen Marshall is one of New Zealand's most admired contemporary short-story writers. His selected stories, *The Divided World*, appeared in 1989. He lives in Timaru.

Glyn Maxwell's first book of poems, *Tale of the Mayor's Son*, was a Poetry Book Society Choice in 1990. He lives in Welwyn Garden City.

Gerald Murnane rarely ventures away from Melbourne, Australia, where he lives. He has published several works of fiction, including *The Plains* and – most recently – *Velvet Waters*.

Gregory O'Brien is well known in New Zealand as a painter as well as a poet. He has also published a novel, *Diesel Mystic*.

Michael Ondaatje was born in Sri Lanka, and lives in Toronto. He is well known for his prose as well as his poetry, and is a contributing editor to the journal, *Brick*.

Vincent O'Sullivan is a New Zealander whose *Selected Poems* will be published next year. He has written stage plays, including the very successful *Shuriken*, and several books of short stories.

Padgett Powell lives in Gainesville, Florida. 'Wait' and 'South Carolina' are included in his new book, *Typical*, which was published this year in the USA.

Salman Rushdie's most recent book is a collection of essays, *Imaginary Homelands*.

Philip Salom was raised on a dairy farm in Western Australia. His poetry collections include *The Silent Piano*, *The Projectionist* and *Sky Poems*.

Elizabeth Smither's most recent volume of poetry is *A Pattern of Marching*, which won the New Zealand Book Award. She lives in New Plymouth, and also writes fiction.

Sharon Thesen lives in Vancouver, and teaches at Capilano College. Her selected poems, *The Pangs of Sunday*, was published last year.

Hone Tuwhare was born in Kaikohe, in the north of New Zealand, and is one of New Zealand's best-known poets. *No Ordinary Sun* (1964) was hailed as the first book of poetry in English by a Maori writer, and was reprinted many times. His most recent collection of poems is *Mihi*.

Ian Wedde is a poet and also the author of two novels, *Symmes Hole* and *Survival Arts*. His essay was commissioned by the National Art Gallery, New Zealand, in conjunction with its proposed exhibition project, 'In Our Own Image'.

Albert Wendt is a leading Samoan writer who lives and teaches in Auckland. His novels include *Pouliuli*, *Leaves of the Banyan Tree*, and – just published – *Ola*. He has also edited anthologies of new Pacific writing.

Damien Wilkins is a New Zealander living in St Louis, Missouri. His book of short fiction, *The Veteran Perils*, appeared last year.

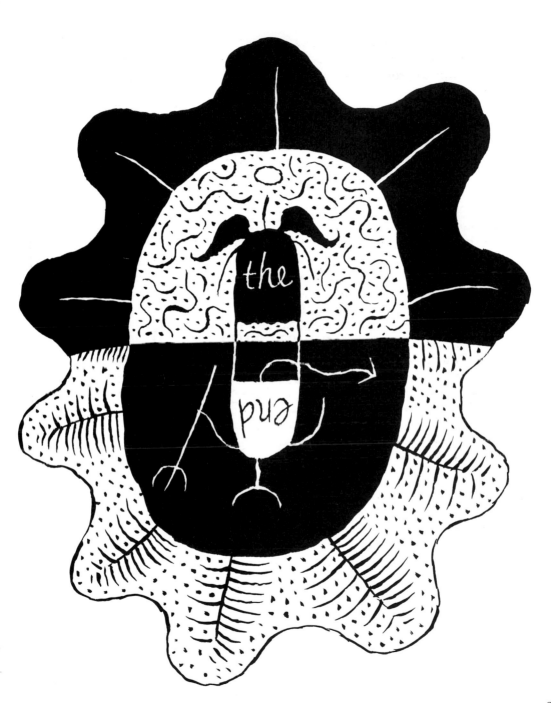